INDEX

Questions marked with an asterisk (*) are worked examples, fully analysed. The remaining questions are for your practice, and have hints and answers.

It is best to work through the questions in order: later questions assume you have already worked through the earlier ones.

NOT TO BE
TAKEN AWAY

Version 2.00

ABOUT THIS BOOK

You've learnt everything in the Standard Level syllabus, and you've done lots of short practice questions – and although some of them send you back to your books for further revision, you can generally understand what the question is asking of you and what you need to know.

But then you turn to the longer section B questions: some of them just *look* frightening, but aren't too bad when you analyse them; others have you scratching your head because you can't figure out what they actually mean; and then there are those where you *do* know what they mean, but haven't got the first idea how to set about answering them.

This book aims to help you view such questions as friendly pets rather than scary aliens! We'll take the questions to bits to see what the examiner is trying to get out of you; we'll see how you can use the structure of the question to get clues which will help you to answer it; and, believe it or not, you can still get marks even if you can't get to the answers. In each case you might like to try answering the question yourself before reading about it.

The book is divided up into sections each of which analyses a different type of question and looks at the techniques you'll need. Side notes in grey boxes reveal tips which can be applied more generally. After some fully worked questions in each chapter, there are further questions for you to try: in these, I give you hints and answers.

But before we get started I'd like to give you some crucial bits of advice, because in the end you're the one that has to answer the questions – this book can only help you on your way.

- Maths exams are all about knowing the *detail* rather than the generalities. If you miss a bit out of your revision, and you need that particular fact in the exam, it's too late! So make sure you thoroughly revise the whole syllabus.
- The more you practice answering long questions, the more confident you will be in the exam. And if you try all the long questions you can lay your hands on, you are more likely to face similar ones in the exam. Always follow up with your teacher or with a friend those parts of questions which you can't do– otherwise next time the same sort of question comes up, you still won't be able to do it!
- Many people struggle because their algebra isn't good enough to tackle the harder calculus, equation solving and so on. If that's you, do something about it.

Through Oxford Study Courses I have been privileged to help many students revise towards their IB Mathematics exams, and much of what I have learnt from teaching them has been distilled into this book. I would value any feedback so that later editions can continue to help students around the world.

Please feel free to e-mail me on inlucas@greentrees.fsnet.co.uk. All correspondence will be answered personally.

Ian Lucas

LONG QUESTIONS – WHAT TO LOOK FOR

Why do examiners need to test you with long questions?
Generally, short questions test you on just one or two facts or techniques related to a specific topic. The long questions will often test your wider understanding of how different areas within a syllabus topic relate to each other, and can also straddle more than one section of the syllabus. But by dividing the questions into parts the examiners are helping you through.

How are long questions constructed? Look closely at any long question: it is likely to be divided up into lettered sections, which may in turn be divided into sub-sections with Roman numerals (i, ii, iii etc). Generally, the lettered sections are fairly independent of each other (although a result from one section may be used in a later one); but the numbered sections will either be strongly related to each other, or actually follow on from each other.

How can the key words help me? Many mathematics exam questions start with a key word:
- *Write down* means that you should be able to write down the answer with little or no working
- *Hence* means that you must use the previous answer
- *Explain:* no need to woffle – a concise sentence will usually do.
- *Sketch (a graph)* – you need to show the shape of the curve with one or two key points (such as axis intercepts) marked. Whereas *plot* means that you have to draw an accurate graph with axis scales.
- *Find, evaluate, calculate* all imply that there is a certain amount of working to show.
- *Show that* means that the answer is given for you, and you must produce enough working to show how to get that answer. But, importantly, you may also be able to use this answer in the next part of the question, even if you *haven't* been able to work it out yourself.

Are all long questions difficult? No, although some parts towards the end of a question may be hard. This is to ensure that those who get the highest grades have had some difficult "hoops" to jump through. The thing to remember is that the answer to all the questions *must* lie within the syllabus somewhere. The difficulty comes from three particular areas:
- You don't understand the language or notation within the question. The practice within this book should help you with that.
- You get stuck with the algebra (either because you don't know what to do next, or because you've made a mistake which has made the next moves much harder, or even impossible). We shall learn how to check and re-check what we've done, looking for common errors.
- Some questions will ask you to extend what you know to do something new. The only preparation for that is thorough revision and plenty of practice.

But let's be honest – it's very likely that there will be some parts of questions which you can't do. Very few people get 100%. It's important to accept that and work to get as many marks as you can in the questions you *can* do. So we'll be talking about that as well.

BOOKWORK QUESTIONS

Our first look at section B questions concentrates on those which are essentially the same as a whole series of section A questions stuck together. In other words, the question doesn't develop as you move from one part to the next – you are being asked some straightforward bookwork questions. There might be some algebra or calculator work, but nothing too complex. You won't be asked to do things you haven't done before. The strategy is simple: work through each question methodically, remaining alert to situations where the information gleaned from one part *does* in fact relate to a later part.

Question 1

A ball is thrown vertically upwards into the air. The height, h metres, of the ball above the ground after t seconds is given by

$$h = 2 + 30t - 5t^2$$

(a)   Find the initial height above the ground of the ball.   *[2 marks]*

(b)   Show that the height of the ball after one second is 27m   *[2 marks]*

(c)   At a time t later the ball is again at a height of 27m

    (i)   Write down an equation that t must satisfy when the ball is at a height of 27m

    (ii)   Solve the equation algebraically.   *[4 marks]*

(d)   (i)   Find $\dfrac{dh}{dt}$

    (ii)   Find the initial velocity of the ball.

    (iii)   Find when the ball reaches it maximum height.

    (iv)   Find the maximum height of the ball.   *[7 marks]*

> In kinematics questions, the word "initial" always refers to the situation when $t = 0$

Analysis: The first thing to do is to look quickly through the question to see what it is about. Here, the information presented at the start of the question makes it clear that we are dealing with a kinematics problem (syllabus section 6.6). It's not surprising to see a differential in part (d) – in fact, it would be very surprising to have a kinematics questions without any calculus in it. We can also see that no other syllabus sections are involved.

Next look at the mark allocation – there are generally 2 marks for each answer, so it doesn't look as if any one part is going to be horribly difficult (although we don't know how the 7 marks in (d) are allocated).

Now have a look at the keywords: *Find, show, write down, solve.* No sign of a *hence* so you won't necessarily have to work out how a particular answer from one part can be manipulated to answer the next part. This doesn't mean that there is no connection between them: for example, you will need (d)(i) to answer the other parts in (d), and (d)(iii) to answer (d)(iv). But there is no overall aim to the question where perhaps the concluding part is based on your answers to all the other parts, or where you are expected to see how an algebraic result you have derived in one part can be used in the next.

So you must aim to answer the questions accurately, and check your answers wherever you can. In part (c)(ii) we have to solve an equation algebraically: it's likely to be a quadratic equation (see the t^2 in the original equation?) so it should factorise easily. If it doesn't, we need to check that we've derived the right equation in (c)(i).

Answer: When you are given a formula in a question which models a real life situation, try and get a feel for how the formula works.

$$h = 2 + 30t - 5t^2$$

The domain is $t \geq 0$: that is, the ball's motion is measured from a time of 0 seconds, and t cannot be negative. Simple enough. Next we see that the height of the ball is given by a quadratic function: at first, the $30t$ dominates so the height increases; then the $5t^2$ term is going to take over as t gets bigger, and since this is a negative term, the height will start to decrease, eventually becoming negative. In practice, the height will become 0 again when the ball hits the ground, and after that the formula is no longer valid.

Part (a): We want to find the height when t = 0 so we just have to substitute into the formula.

(a)	Find the initial height above the ground of the ball.

When $t = 0$, $h = 2 + 0 - 0 =$ **2m**

(b)	Show that the height of the ball after one second is 27m

$$h = 2 + 30 \times 1 - 5 \times 1^2$$
$$= 2 + 30 - 5$$
$$= 27$$

So, after 1s the height of the ball is **27m**

> When answering a "show" question your working is crucial – there must be enough to demonstrate how you get to the answer.

In part (c) we face a typical situation in questions involving formulae. First, nice cop smiles at you and asks you to substitute a value for the variable on the right hand side. Easy. Then nasty cop comes along and asks you a question which boils down to substituting a value for the variable on the left hand side – but that invariably leads to some equation solving. And, depending on what sort of function you have, that may be fairly simple or it may be pretty horrific!

> Don't forget that in the paper 2, you can solve nasty equations with your GDC (unless the question asks you to solve algebraically).

(c)(i): Note the keyword *write down*.

(c)(ii): In this case we are told to substitute $h = 27$. But have you spotted that this is the same as the height we worked out in part (b)? So we should expect $t = 1$ to be one of the answers – a good check that we have solved the quadratic correctly.

(c)	At a time t later the ball is again at a height of 27m	
	(i)	Write down an equation that t must satisfy when the ball is at a height of 27m

$27 = 2 + 30t - 5t^2$

	(ii)	Solve the equation algebraically.

$$5t^2 - 30t + 25 = 0$$
$$t^2 - 6t + 5 = 0$$
$$(t - 5)(t - 1) = 0$$
$$t = 1 \text{ or } 5$$
Thus the ball is at a height of 27m again after **5s**

> When solving a quadratic, rearrange so that the squared term is positive, and one side equals zero

Even though the question just asked us to solve the equation, it's a good idea to interpret the answer in the context of the situation which the equation is modelling. And here, of course, the ball reaches 27m at 1s on its way up, and then again at 5s on its way down.

Part (d): Here we see a differential appearing. You should know that when you have a function giving values of height or displacement, differentiating that function gives velocity; and differentiating again gives acceleration. So it's no surprise that the word "velocity" appears in part (d).

(d)(ii): The differential from part (i) gives us an expression for the velocity.

(d)(iii): At its maximum height the ball stops moving, so $v = 0$.

(d)	(i)	Find $\dfrac{dh}{dt}$
		$\dfrac{dh}{dt} = 30 - 10t$

	(ii)	Find the initial velocity of the ball.
		When $t = 0$, $v = 30 \text{ms}^{-1}$

	(iii)	Find when the ball reaches it maximum height.
		$0 = 30 - 10t$ $t = 3$ So maximum height is reached at **3s**

	(iv)	Find the maximum height of the ball.
		When $t = 3$, $h = 2 + 30 \times 3 - 5 \times 3^2 = 47$ So maximum height is **47m**

Note that I always show the working when I substitute numbers into a formula. Firstly, you might get a mark or two even if you end up with the wrong answer. Secondly, it shows the examiner what you are doing: you have to do the working anyway, so why not write it down. Thirdly, it helps you to think logically and hence you are more likely to work accurately.

Question 2

The diagram shows part of the graph of the curve $y = a(x - h)^2 + k$, where $a, h, k \in \mathbb{Z}$

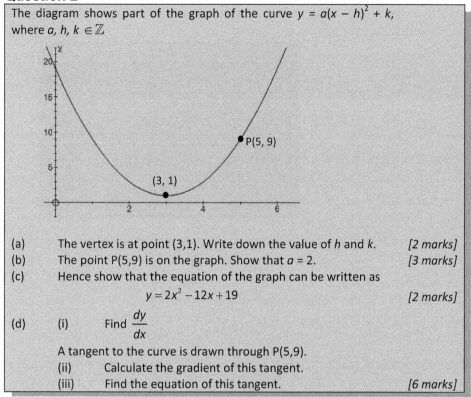

(a)   The vertex is at point (3,1). Write down the value of h and k.   *[2 marks]*

(b)   The point P(5,9) is on the graph. Show that $a = 2$.   *[3 marks]*

(c)   Hence show that the equation of the graph can be written as

$$y = 2x^2 - 12x + 19$$ *[2 marks]*

(d)   (i)   Find $\dfrac{dy}{dx}$

A tangent to the curve is drawn through P(5,9).

(ii)   Calculate the gradient of this tangent.

(iii)   Find the equation of this tangent.   *[6 marks]*

Analysis: A quick look through the question tells us that this is all about a quadratic graph and the typical questions which go with it. There's some differentiation followed by questions about gradients and tangents. Quadratic graphs and equations crop up all over the syllabus, although most of the material for this question comes from sections 2.4 and 6.6. It's important that you understand how a quadratic graph relates to its equation, all the various facts about symmetry, intercepts, the vertex, graph transformations; and how differentiation is linked to gradients and hence tangents of graphs. Although the parts of the question do relate to each other, we are looking here at standard bookwork – there's nothing unfamiliar in the question at all (as long as you've done your revision properly).

Once again the mark allocation is about 2 marks per part, although there are 3 marks for (b) – probably several lines of working required.

Keywords? *Write down, show, hence, find, calculate.* Note that if you get a *hence* you *must* use what you have done already to answer the question.

Answer: When answering long questions in particular, it's easy to scan over words and phrases without reading them properly, The introductory information gives us a quadratic equation with three constants a, h and k (presumably we're going to have to work these out) - but it also tells us that a, h and k, $\in \mathbb{Z}$ in other words they are integers. Useful – if we think that h for example is 1.5 then that can't be right.

Part (a): *Write down* implies very little or no working. To answer this you must understand how transformations of graphs affect their equations. Standard bookwork.

Part (b): Whenever you are given a point on a graph, and you know something about the equation of the graph, remember that it is usually worthwhile substituting the coordinates of the point into the equation. In this case we know the values of h and k and we can substitute for x and y – that just leaves a to be calculated.

The diagram shows part of the graph of the curve $y = a(x-h)^2 + k$, where $a, h, k \in \mathbb{Z}$

(a)   The vertex is at point (3,1). Write down the value of h and k.

$h = 3; k = 1$

(b)   The point P(5,9) is on the graph. Show that $a = 2$.

$$y = a(x-h)^2 + k$$
$$9 = a(5-3)^2 + 1$$
$$9 = 4a + 1$$
$$8 = 4a$$
So **$a = 2$**

Part (c): Our first "*hence*"! In other words, you *must* use what you have done so far to work out the equation of the graph. We've found a, h and k, so all we need to do is substitute into the quadratic and rearrange.

You can sometimes use a "*show that*" question to work backwards to a previous answer which you have had trouble with. In this case, for example, you could rewrite $y = 2x^2 - 12x + 19$ in the form $y = a(x - h)^2 + k$ to find h and k.

(c)   Hence show that the equation of the graph can be written as
$$y = 2x^2 - 12x + 19$$

$$y = 2(x-3)^2 + 1$$
$$y = 2x^2 - 12x + 18 + 1$$
$$y = 2x^2 - 12x + 19$$

Part (d): What is the relationship between differentiation and tangents? Quite simply, the derived function *always* represents the rate of change of the original function, and thus can be used to calculate the gradient of the graph at any point. Once you know the gradient at a point, you can work out the equation of the tangent at that point.

(d)(iii): I prefer using $y - y_1 = m(x - x_1)$ to $y = mx + c$ because you actually write down the equation of the line in the first line of working – then it's just a matter of rearranging.

(d)   (i)   Find $\dfrac{dy}{dx}$

$$\dfrac{dy}{dx} = 4x - 12$$

A tangent to the curve is drawn through P(5,9).
(ii)   Calculate the gradient of this tangent.

When $x = 5$, $\dfrac{dy}{dx} = 8$

Check on the diagram that the answer looks reasonable – if it's paper 2, you could use your GDC to draw the graph and the tangent as a check.

(iii)   Find the equation of this tangent.

$$y - y_1 = m(x - x_1)$$
$$y - 9 = 8(x - 5)$$
$$y - 9 = 8x - 40$$
So the equation of the tangent is **$y = 8x - 31$**

Question 3

In a school of 176 students, 64 study Mathematics (*M*), 56 study Economics (*E*) and 78 do not study either subject. The Venn diagram illustrates this information.

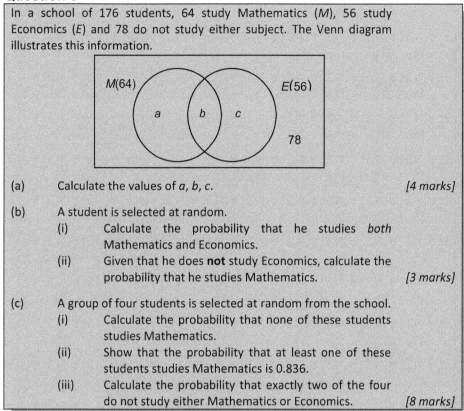

(a)   Calculate the values of *a*, *b*, *c*.   [4 marks]

(b)   A student is selected at random.
    (i)   Calculate the probability that he studies *both* Mathematics and Economics.
    (ii)   Given that he does **not** study Economics, calculate the probability that he studies Mathematics.   [3 marks]

(c)   A group of four students is selected at random from the school.
    (i)   Calculate the probability that none of these students studies Mathematics.
    (ii)   Show that the probability that at least one of these students studies Mathematics is 0.836.
    (iii)   Calculate the probability that exactly two of the four do not study either Mathematics or Economics.   [8 marks]

Analysis: A scan through the questions shows us that in each part we are asked to calculate probabilities. Note the difference between (b), "a student is selected at random", and (c) where "four students are selected at random". This suggests that part (c) is going to involve binomial probabilities. And what about the Venn diagram in part (a)? Students often find Venn diagrams off-putting, but once the numbers have been filled in (always start at the centre and work outwards) it's actually very simple to use the diagrams to calculate probabilities. (b)(ii) starts with "given that" – this usually implies conditional probability (but see question 26), and Venn diagrams are great for such calculations.

There are 8 marks for part (c), so expect something a bit meaty in there.

All the keywords are *calculate* with a *show* in the last part. With numbers such as 56 and 78, we're going to need our calculator. There's no help in the earlier parts, and no way of checking our answers (except to note that if we get any answers bigger than 1 they must be wrong). So show all the working where necessary and check everything you do.

Answer: Don't get confused reading a Venn diagram. The students in circle *M* study Mathematics, *whatever else they do*. *a* represents those who just study Mathematics, *b* those who study both Mathematics and Economics.

Part (a):   The total in the circles must be 176 − 78 = 98. But 64 + 56 = 120, so 22 have been included twice over, and must therefore be the number of students in the intersection. Note that I have redrawn the Venn diagram with all the numbers included: this doesn't need to form part of the answer, but it is very useful to have it to hand when carrying out the probability calculations.

In a school of 176 students, 64 study Mathematics (*M*), 56 study Economics (*E*) and 78 do not study either subject. The Venn diagram illustrates this information.

(a)   Calculate the values of *a*, *b*, *c*.

$a + b + c = 176 - 78 = 98$
Since $M + E = 120$, $b = 120 - 98 = $ **22**
So, $a = 64 - 22 = $ **42**
        $c = 56 - 22 = $ **34**

Always check that the numbers add to give the correct total. (When I first wrote this down I put *a* = 46, but discovered my mistake by checking the total. Really!).

Part (b): The basic probability of an event occurring is the number of ways it can happen divided by the total number of possibilities.

(b)(ii): Conditional probability is the probability of an event occurring when something else has already happened. Using the principle above, we're looking for the number who study Mathematics out of the total who do not study Economics. The conditional probability formula can be used, but it's much easier just to use the numbers in the Venn diagram (ie 42 out of 42 + 78).

(b)   A student is selected at random.
        (i)   Calculate the probability that he studies *both* Mathematics and Economics.

P(studies Mathematics and Economics) = $\dfrac{22}{176}$ = **0.125**

        (ii)   Given that he studies Mathematics, calculate the probability that he does **not** study Economics.

P(Mathematics | not Economics) = $\dfrac{42}{120}$ = **0.35**

Part(c):   Once we are asked for probabilities of "*x* times out of *y*" happening this is usually to do with binomial probabilities. In (i) and (ii) we are dealing with the probability of a student studying Mathematics (64 out of 176), in part (iii) a student studying neither subject (78 out of 176).

(c)(ii): P(at least 1) = 1 – P(none)
(c)(iii): Although binomial probabilities can be worked out using a GDC it you can also show the calculation you are using. I've included the binomial calculation here just to see what it looks like.

It's a good idea to state formally the distribution you are using whenever you are answering a binomial or Normal probability question. This shows you are on the ball, and may get you a mark even if your subsequent calculations are wrong.

(c)	A group of four students is selected at random from the school.
	(i) Calculate the probability that none of these students studies Mathematics.

$X \sim B(4, \frac{64}{176})$

P(0 out of 4 study Mathematics) = **0.164** (GDC)

	(ii) Calculate the probability that at least one of these students studies Mathematics.

P(at least 1 out of 4 study Mathematics) = $1 - 0.164 =$ **0.836**

	(iii) Calculate the probability that exactly two of the four do not study either Mathematics or Economics is 0.365.

$X \sim B(4, \frac{78}{176})$

P(neither Mathematics or Economics) = $\dfrac{78}{176} = 0.4432$

P(2 out of 4) = ${}^4C_2 \times 0.4432^2 \times 0.5568^2$

$\qquad\qquad\qquad = 6 \times 0.1964 \times 0.3100$

$\qquad\qquad\qquad = $ **0.365**

Now here's one for you to try – get as far as you can without looking at the hints.

Question 4

The following diagram shows a pentagon PQRST, with PQ = 10.5 cm, QR = 3.8 cm, QS = 8.0 cm, $P\hat{T}S = 105°$, $P\hat{S}T = 58°$ and $P\hat{Q}S = 64°$

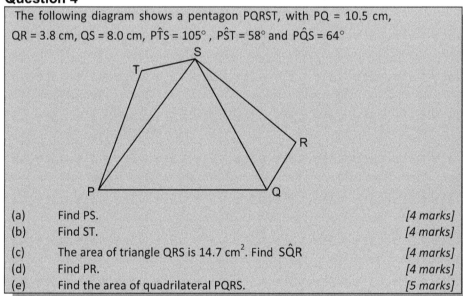

(a)	Find PS.	[4 marks]
(b)	Find ST.	[4 marks]
(c)	The area of triangle QRS is 14.7 cm². Find $S\hat{Q}R$	[4 marks]
(d)	Find PR.	[4 marks]
(e)	Find the area of quadrilateral PQRS.	[5 marks]

Hints: A quick look through the question (you've seen me write that down a few times now) indicates that this is all about the formulae for non right-angled triangles. I would draw a large copy of the diagram, fill in the given information and then fill in each result as you work them out. Check that they look reasonable.

> Use the sin rule when the question involves 2 sides and 2 angles, the cos rule when it involves 3 sides and 1 angle.

(a)   Use the cosine rule on triangle PSQ.

(b)   Use the sine rule on triangle PST, but you'll need to work out $S\hat{P}T$.

(c)   The area formula – but the area is given, so we need to use it "backwards". Just write out the formula then fill in the bits you know. You'll then have an equation to solve.

(d)   PR is not a line on the diagram, so draw it in and then decide which triangle to use. PQR seems the obvious one, but you'll need the answer to (c) to get $P\hat{Q}R$; that's why it's a good idea to fill in the answers on your diagram as you go along. And let me stress again – *show your working*. If part (c) is wrong then (d) will be wrong as well – but you can still get all the marks for correct working.

(e)   The only part where you have to do a bit of extra thinking! You haven't got a formula for the area of a quadrilateral, but a quadrilateral is just two triangles added together. Which two are you going to use? I'd start with QRS since we already know that area. And, again, show your working carefully.

Answers:
(a)   AD = 10.0 cm
(b)   DE = 3.04 cm
(c) $S\hat{Q}R = 75.3°$
(d)   PR = 10.2 cm
(e)   Area of PQRS = 52.4 cm^2

Let's do one more question together and then I'll finish this chapter with some more examples of straight bookwork questions for you to try yourself. But first, let me ask: "How do I recognise that an exam question *is* a bookwork question?"

Generally, you'll find that such questions look familiar because – as long as you have done plenty of practice questions – the same topics tend to appear in them. None of the parts will have too many marks attached to them; there won't be any complex algebra or unfamiliar diagrams. However, you'll sometimes find that *most* of the question is straightforward, but then there can be a sting in the tail, an unfamiliar twist to a standard situation designed to make you think beyond what you have done before. I think the next question is like that, the giveaway being that the final part has 7 marks attached to it.

Question 5

In this question the vector $\begin{pmatrix} 1 \\ 0 \end{pmatrix}$ represents a displacement of 1 km east

and the vector $\begin{pmatrix} 0 \\ 1 \end{pmatrix}$ represents a displacement of 1 km north.

The diagram shows the positions of towns A, B and C and an airport O at (0, 0).

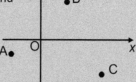

A is 600 km west and 200 km south of the airport.
B is 200 km east and 400 km north of the airport.
C is 1200 km east and 350 km south of the airport.

(a)　(i)　Find $\overrightarrow{AB}$

　　　(ii)　Show that the vector of length one unit in the direction of
　　　　　　$\overrightarrow{AB}$ is $\begin{pmatrix} 0.8 \\ 0.6 \end{pmatrix}$

[4 marks]

An aircraft flies over town A at 12:00, heading towards B at 250 km h^{-1}.

Let $\begin{pmatrix} p \\ q \end{pmatrix}$ be the velocity vector of the aircraft. Let t be the number of

hours in flight after 12:00. The position of the aircraft can be given by the vector equation

$$\begin{pmatrix} x \\ y \end{pmatrix} = \begin{pmatrix} -600 \\ -200 \end{pmatrix} + t \begin{pmatrix} p \\ q \end{pmatrix}$$

(b)　(i)　Show that the velocity vector is $\begin{pmatrix} 200 \\ 150 \end{pmatrix}$

　　　(ii)　Find the position vector of the aircraft at 13:00.

　　　(iii)　At what time is the aircraft flying over town B.

[6 marks]

Over town B the aircraft changes direction so it now flies towards town C. It takes five hours to travel the 1250 km from B to C. Over town A the aircraft had 17 000 litres of fuel left. The aircraft uses 1800 litres of fuel per hour when travelling at 250 km h^{-1}. When the fuel gets below 1000 litres a warning light comes on.

(c)　How far from Town C will the aircraft be when the warning light comes on?

[7 marks]

Analysis: Generally, the longer vector questions will concentrate either on pure vector geometry or an application of vectors, of which the most common involves displacement and velocity (see syllabus sections 4.2 – 4.4). In such a situation, a car, bike, plane or boat is travelling in a straight line at a constant speed, in which case the vector equation

describing its displacement will be $\begin{pmatrix} x \\ y \end{pmatrix} = \begin{pmatrix} x_0 \\ y_0 \end{pmatrix} + t \begin{pmatrix} v_x \\ v_y \end{pmatrix}$ where $\begin{pmatrix} x \\ y \end{pmatrix}$ is the

displacement (position relative to the origin) at time t, $\begin{pmatrix} x_0 \\ y_0 \end{pmatrix}$ is the initial

position, and $\begin{pmatrix} v_x \\ v_y \end{pmatrix}$ is the vector describing the velocity. Thus, a velocity

vector of $\begin{pmatrix} 4 \\ 6 \end{pmatrix}$ means that the position will change by that amount every

second (minute or hour, depending on the units of t). In practical applications such as these, you should always be asking yourself how the question relates to the actual situation.

The introduction to the question sets the scene, and tells us that we are using a unit vector based on 1km East and 1km North, the standard for this sort of question. Then it tells us the positions of A, B and C – effectively A = (-600, -200) and so on. Part (a) is vector geometry bookwork. Before part (b) we're given more information – and the crucial bit is that the speed is 250 km h^{-1}. When this is linked with (a)(ii) the answer to (b)(i) should be obvious – but they give it to you anyway so that you can still use it to answer (b)(ii) and (iii) which are really just opposite sides of the same coin. These are the standard things you are asked to do in this type of question.

Part (c) has a lot of introductory information and a lot of numbers – you are being tested to see whether you can put those numbers to use correctly. If you read it carefully you can see that at its heart it's just a speed, distance, time question – but worth 7 marks.

Look back over past papers – you'll find several very similar questions. I suggest you try 3 or 4 of them.

Answer: Part (a): In (a)(ii) you're being asked for a *unit vector*, a vector of length 1 in a particular direction.

Make sure you use the correct notation in vector questions: column vectors are written vertically, coordinates of points horizontally.

(a)(i):   To find the vector between two points, subtract the coordinates of the first point from the second.

(a)(ii): The find the unit vector, divide the original vector by its length – so first of all you need to find the length using Pythagoras.

A is 600 km west and 200 km south of the airport.
B is 200 km east and 400 km north of the airport.
C is 1200 km east and 350 km south of the airport.

(a)   (i)   Find $\overrightarrow{AB}$

$$\overrightarrow{AB} = \begin{pmatrix} 200 \\ 400 \end{pmatrix} - \begin{pmatrix} -600 \\ -200 \end{pmatrix} = \begin{pmatrix} \mathbf{800} \\ \mathbf{600} \end{pmatrix}$$

(ii)   Show that the vector of length one unit in the direction of $\overrightarrow{AB}$ is $\begin{pmatrix} 0.8 \\ 0.6 \end{pmatrix}$

Length of $\overrightarrow{AB}$ is $\sqrt{(600^2 - 800^2)} = 1000$

Or find the length using a 3, 4, 5 triangle.

So unit vector = $\dfrac{1}{1000}\begin{pmatrix} 800 \\ 600 \end{pmatrix} = \begin{pmatrix} 0.8 \\ 0.6 \end{pmatrix}$

What does the unit vector represent? It is a vector in the direction AB with length 1km. Now, the plane in part (b) is travelling at 250 km h^{-1}, so in 1 hour it will travel 250 times the unit vector – this, then will be the velocity vector (that is, the change in position in 1 hour).

(b)(ii): Now that we have the velocity vector we can complete the vector equation giving the plane's position. Then substitute t = 1 to find the position at 13:00.

(b)(iii): Remember what I said in question 1 about questions involving a formula? It's the same principle here: substitute the position vector for B in the left hand side of the vector equation and hence find the value of t.

(b)	(i)	Show that the velocity vector is $\begin{pmatrix} 200 \\ 150 \end{pmatrix}$

The velocity vector is $250 \times \begin{pmatrix} 0.8 \\ 0.6 \end{pmatrix} = \begin{pmatrix} 200 \\ 150 \end{pmatrix}$ km h^{-1}

	(ii)	Find the position vector of the aircraft at 13:00.

The vector equation of AB is $\begin{pmatrix} x \\ y \end{pmatrix} = \begin{pmatrix} -600 \\ -200 \end{pmatrix} + t\begin{pmatrix} 200 \\ 150 \end{pmatrix}$

So when $t = 1$, aircraft is at $\begin{pmatrix} x \\ y \end{pmatrix} = \begin{pmatrix} -600 \\ -200 \end{pmatrix} + 1\begin{pmatrix} 200 \\ 150 \end{pmatrix} = \begin{pmatrix} -400 \\ -50 \end{pmatrix}$

	(iii)	At what time is the aircraft flying over town B.

Town B has position vector $\begin{pmatrix} 200 \\ 400 \end{pmatrix}$

$$\begin{pmatrix} 200 \\ 400 \end{pmatrix} = \begin{pmatrix} -600 \\ -200 \end{pmatrix} + t\begin{pmatrix} 200 \\ 150 \end{pmatrix}$$

$$\begin{pmatrix} 800 \\ 600 \end{pmatrix} = t\begin{pmatrix} 200 \\ 150 \end{pmatrix}$$

So, $t = 4$ and the plane arrives at **16:00**

> Note that the question asked for the time of arrival at B, not the value of t.

Part (c): This is a question about the rate at which the aircraft uses fuel. Analyse it carefully and you will find that the information you are given is:

- Aircraft speed (250 km h^{-1})
- Rate of using fuel (1800 litres per hour)
- Distances between towns (A to B: 1000 km; B to C: 1250 km)
- Amount of fuel at A (17 000 litres)

It's now straightforward to put that information together and work out when there are just 1000 litres left – and vectors aren't even involved!

Over town B the aircraft changes direction so it now flies towards town C. It takes five hours to travel the 1250 km from B to C. Over town A the aircraft had 17 000 litres of fuel left. The aircraft uses 1800 litres of fuel per hour when travelling at 250 km h^{-1}. When the fuel gets below 1000 litres a warning light comes on.

(c)	How far from Town C will the aircraft be when the warning light comes on?

From A to B takes 4 hours, so uses 7200 litres of fuel.
There are then 17000 − 7200 = 9800 litres remaining
To reduce to 1000 litres will use 8800 litres
This will take $8800 \div 1800 = 4.89$ hours
At 250 km h^{-1} the plane travels 1222 km in 4.89 hours
So the warning light goes on when the plane is **28km** from C.

There are other ways to deal with the data – for example, you can calculate that the aircraft uses 7.2 litre per km, and work with that figure. Don't forget that there is often more than one correct method to solve a problem, and you could also use an alternative method to check your answer.

Question 6

In a certain school, all Year 10 students take the same end of year Mathematics exam which is marked out of 100. It is found that the marks for both boys and girls are normally distributed. For the boys, the mean is 66 with standard deviation 8.2; for the girls, the mean is 69 with standard deviation 7.8.

a) Calculate the probability that a girl has a mark greater than 75. [3 marks]

b) Find the percentage of boys with a mark greater than 75. [3 marks]

c) 10% of the girls scored more than x marks. Find x. [3 marks]

55% of the students in Year 10 are girls, 45% are boys.
A Year 10 student is selected at random.

d) Show that the probability that the student has a mark greater than 75 is 0.183 [4 marks]

e) Given that the student *does* have a mark greater than 75, what is the probability that the student is a boy? [3 marks]

Hints: The introduction to the question tells us that we are dealing with normal probability – you can never assume a normal distribution, the question must specify that you are to use it. When we get to part (d) we must work out the relevance of the 55%/45% split of girls to boys; and in part (e) there is a "given that" – looks like conditional probability.

(a) A straightforward normal probability. All normal probabilities are calculated using the GDC; make sure you are very familiar with the calculator methods required.

(b) Exactly the same type of calculation as (a), but with the answer expressed as a percentage instead of a probability.

(c) Normal probability "backwards". Draw a sketch of the curve, shade the relevant 10% area, and then use your calculator to find x. Check that your answer is reasonable (ie a sensible distance above the mean).

(d) I suggest a tree diagram would be useful here. First select either boy or girl, then select greater than 75 or not.

(e) Using a tree diagram to work out conditional probability comes under the heading of standard bookwork, or use the formula.

Answers:
(a) 0.221
(b) 0.136
(c) Calculator gives 78.996, so 10% got more than 78 (fewer than 10% would have got more than 79).
(d) $0.55 \times 0.221 + 0.45 \times 0.136 = 0.183$
(e) $\dfrac{0.45 \times 0.136}{0.183} = 0.334$

Question 7

The equation of a curve is written in the form $a(x - m)(x - n)$. The curve intersects the x-axis at $(1, 0)$ and $(-3, 0)$. The curve of $y = f(x)$ is shown in the diagram below.

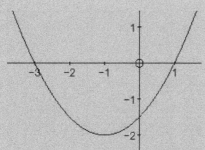

a) (i)   Write down the values of m and n.

(ii)   Given that the point $(3, 6)$ is on the curve, find the value of a.

(iii) Write down the equation of the curve in the form
$y = ax^2 + bx + c$ *[5 marks]*

b) (i)   Find $\dfrac{dy}{dx}$

(ii)   Find the coordinates of the point on the curve where the tangent has a gradient of 3.   *[4 marks]*

c) The line L passes through $(1, 0)$, and is perpendicular to the tangent to the curve at that point.

(i)   Find the equation of L

(ii)   Find the x-coordinate of the point where L intersects the curve again.   *[6 marks]*

Hints: Once again, like question 2, the whole question is testing your understanding of quadratic curves and equations. The quadratic is first given to us in factorised form – do you understand the connection between the factors and the x-intercepts? And, like question 2, part (a)(ii) gives us a point to substitute which will result in an equation for a.

Never forget that when you differentiate *any* function however simple, however complex, the differential $\dfrac{dy}{dx}$ gives you the gradient function for the curve. But in part (b)(ii) we are told that the gradient of the tangent is 2, so we have to work back to find where that occurs.

> The question asks for "the coordinates"; having found the x coordinate don't forget to work out y as well to gain full marks.

Part (c): something a bit different, and you will find it enormously helpful to sketch line L on the diagram. To find the equation of any straight line you need its gradient and a point on the line. The point is given to us, the gradient will be the gradient of the normal to the curve at $(1, 0)$. In part (c)(ii) we need to find where two lines intersect – this is a standard bookwork technique involving simultaneous equations. Expect two solutions: one of them will give the point $(1, 0)$, the other will give the required intersection.

> (c)(ii) is a good example of a question where you can pick up some marks even if the previous part is wrong – or not done at all. Just show your working clearly.

Answers:

(a) (i) $m = 1$, $n = -3$ (or the other way around)

(ii) $a = \tfrac{1}{2}$ (iii) $y = \tfrac{1}{2}x^2 + x - \tfrac{3}{2}$

(b) (i) $\dfrac{dy}{dx} = x + 1$ (ii) $\left(2, 2\tfrac{1}{2}\right)$

(c) (i) $y = -\tfrac{1}{2}x + \tfrac{1}{2}$ (ii) $x = -4$

Question 8

a)		If $f(x) = \sin^2 x$, show that $f'(x) = 2\sin x\cos x$	*[2 marks]*

The function $g(x)$ is given by

$$g(x) = \sin^2 x + \cos x, \ 0 \leq x \leq \frac{\pi}{2}$$

b)	(i)	Find $g'(x)$	
	(ii)	Use your result from part (i) to show that there is a turning point on $g(x)$ when $x = 0$ and find the x-coordinate of the other turning point in the range $0 \leq x \leq \frac{\pi}{2}$.	
	(iii)	Find $g''(x)$ and hence show that the turning point where $x = 0$ is a minimum.	*[8 marks]*
c)	(i)	Show that $2\sin^2 x - \sin 2x$ can be written as $2\sin x(\sin x - \cos x)$	
	(ii)	**Hence** solve $2\sin^2 x = \sin 2x, \ 0 \leq x \leq \pi$.	*[6 marks]*

Hints: So, this is all about circular functions. I can see a $\sin^2 x$ and a $\sin 2x$, so I should think we'll need to use Pythagorean and double angle identities; part (c) involves a trigonometric equation – that's in syllabus section 3.5. I can also see a second derivative sneaking into the question: better brush up on section 6.2! Although you are given the identities and formulae in the information book, I do advise you to try and commit them to memory, otherwise you might not recognise one in a question when it pops up out of context. The same applies to the laws of logarithms.

This question is non-calculator: you will need to know the values of the sine and cosine of key angles – again, memorise these values for 0°, 30°, 45°, 60° and 90°.

A final point: all the angles in this question are in radians. How do I know? There are three indicators:

Conversions:

π radians = 180°

Degrees to radians: $\times \dfrac{\pi}{180}$

Radians to degrees: $\times \dfrac{180}{\pi}$

- Angles in degrees will *always* be shown with a degrees sign (eg: $\sin x°$)
- The range of values for the function in (b) contains π
- Whenever trigonometric functions are differentiated or integrated, you *must* be working in radians.

However, if you don't like radians, there is nothing to stop you thinking and working in degrees as long as you put your answer in radians (if that is what is expected).

(a)   You will need to use the chain rule. Don't forget that $\sin^2 x$ is a sort of shorthand notation for $(\sin x)^2$.

(b)   (i)   You will need the result from (a).
       (ii)   There are various techniques you need to master to solve trigonometric equations. In this case, without any squares or double angles, you aren't going to need to apply an identity or a formula. However, notice that you can factorise the left hand side.
       (iii)   The second derivative will require use of the product rule since $2\sin x\cos x$ is a product of two functions. Be careful with your working, especially where minus signs are concerned.

(c)   Part (c) has no connection to (a) or (b).
        (i)   Use the double angle formula for sin2x.
        (ii) If you can't see at first how to solve sinx − cosx = 0, try
dividing through the equation by cosx.

Answers:
b)   (i) $g'(x) = 2\sin x \cos x - \sin x$

     (ii) $2\sin x \cos x - \sin x = 0$

                $\sin x(2\cos x - 1) = 0$

                    $\sin x = 0 \Rightarrow x = 0, \quad \cos x = \dfrac{1}{2} \Rightarrow x = \dfrac{\pi}{3}$

     (iii) $g''(x) = -2\sin^2 x + 2\cos^2 x - \cos x$

             $g''(0) = -2\sin^2(0) + 2\cos^2(0) - \cos(0) = 0 + 2 - 1 = 1$

             $\therefore g''(0) > 0$ hence a minimum

c)   (ii) $x = 0, \dfrac{\pi}{4}, \pi$

I think the algebra was a little more difficult in this question than in any of
the previous ones, but nonetheless each part was still testing you on
standard bookwork. In the next chapter we will be looking at questions
where the algebra is definitely more challenging!

Question 9

The distribution of journey times, in minutes, of 1000 commuters to a
city is given in the following frequency table

Journey time	25-30	30-35	35-40	40-45	45-50	50-55	55-60
No of commuters	70	120	220	280	190	90	30

a)   Write down estimates for the mean and standard deviation of
      the journey time.

                                                          [4 marks]

b)   Copy and complete the cumulative frequency table for this
      data.

Journey times (t min)	Number of commuters
$t \le 30$	70
$t \le 35$	190
.	.
.	.

                                                          [2 marks]

c)   (i)   Draw a cumulative frequency graph for this data on
      graph paper. Use a scale of 1cm per 5min on the horizontal
      axis, 1cm per 100 commuters on the vertical axis.
      (ii)   Use your diagram to find an estimate for the median
      journey time and for the number of people whose journey time
      is more than 52 minutes   *[6 marks]*

d)   It is suggested that the distribution of commuting times in
      approximately normal.
      (i)   Assuming a normal distribution, use your answers to
               part (a) to calculate the probability that a commuter
               has a journey of more than 52 minutes.
      (ii)   Compare your answer to that in (c)(ii). Does this
               support the proposal of a normal distribution?   *[4 marks]*

Hints: Some standard work from sections 5.2 and 5.3 of the syllabus
concerning basics statistical diagrams and calculations. Make sure you
fully understand the difference between *frequency* and *cumulative*

frequency and what you would use a cumulative frequency graph for. In part (d) a normal distribution question has sneaked in: this will use the mean and standard deviation found in part (a).

Use your calculator for parts (a) and (d).
(a)   When entering the data into your GDC, use the mid-interval values (eg 27.5 for 25 – 30). The values for mean and standard deviation are only estimates because you don't have exact data.

> In a cumulative frequency table, check that the final value equals the total frequency (1000 in this case).

(b)   Think of the cumulative frequency distribution as an "up to" table: up to 35 mins, for example, there were 190 commuters.

(c)   It would be hard to give the median accurate to more than the nearest minute – partly because of the scale, partly because it's not possible to draw an entirely accurate graph. Make sure the lines on your graph are really clear – there will be marks in it!

(d)   You can create a comparison by converting your answer to (c)(ii) into a probability.

Answers:
(a)   Mean = 41.5, SD = 7.26
(b)   2nd column: 410, 690, 880, 970, 1000

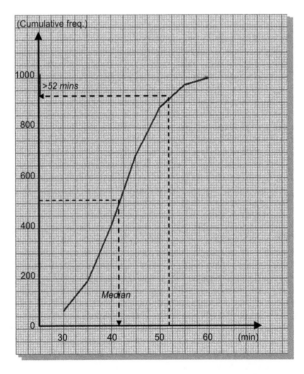

(c)   (ii)   41.6, so 41 or 42 are good answers.
                84 is accurate, so an answer between 70 and 100 is OK.
(d)   (i)   0.074
        (ii)   84 out of 1000 = 0.084. This supports the proposal.

QUESTIONS REQUIRING MORE THOUGHT

Don't all questions require thought? Well, yes of course they do. But in the first chapter I was analysing questions which could essentially be answered by good knowledge and understanding of the syllabus items. In this chapter we shall be looking at questions where you have to go one stage further: first you have to work out what the question is asking you to do, and then you have to decide how to solve it. It's probable that, unlike the bookwork questions, you're going to be faced with new situations to puzzle over, at least in some of the parts of the questions.

And in some ways, this is where we have to overcome the hurdle of "I don't know how to do this question" – where you may need an intuitive leap to work out what to do. It may seem easy when your teacher does it on the board – but you *must* practice these questions to learn how to jump those hurdles yourself.

Let's start with one which involves sequences and series.

Question 10

Martha and David are training for a marathon.

a) Martha runs for 10 hours in the first week. She then increases the time she spends running by 2 hours each week. Find the total number of hours she spends running during the first 6 weeks. *[3 marks]*

b) David also runs for 10 hours in the first week. He then decided to run for 15% longer each week than in the previous week.
   i) Show that in the third week he runs for about 13.2 hours.
   ii) Find the total number of hours he spends running during the first 6 weeks. *[4 marks]*

c) In which week will the time David spends running exceed 36 hours? *[3 marks]*

d) Form an equation in *n*, where *n* represents the number of weeks until they have completed the same total number of hours running. Solve for *n* to find in which week this occurs. *[6 marks]*

Analysis: There is no mention in the question of sequences and series, but reading through the parts there are plenty of clues: "the time increases each week"; "10% longer each week"; when does the time exceed 30 hours". The problem for us is to analyse exactly which of the various formulae applies to each problem. We must also be careful to spot the difference between a question which is effectively asking for a term in a sequence, and one which asks for the sum of a series. For example:

- Arthur walks 5 km on day 1 of a training programme, and then adds 0.5km every day after that. How far does he walk on day 10?
- Arthur walks 5 km on day 1 of a training programme, and then adds 0.5km every day after that. How far has he walked in total by the end of day 10?

These look fairly similar, but the answers are:

$$5 + (10 - 1) \times 0.5 = 9.5 \text{km} \quad \text{and} \quad \tfrac{10}{2}(2 \times 5 + (10 - 1) \times 0.5) = 72.5 \text{ km},$$

In other words, the first question is the 10th term of an arithmetic sequence, the second question is the sum of the first 10 terms.

The trick in answering this question is to look under the surface of the words to see the mathematics which is lurking just below. At the heart of all questions involving sequences and series are the basic nth term and sum to n terms formulae. So, in each part, we need to decide exactly what we're being asked to do, then substitute the right numbers into the right formula. Unlike a "bookwork question", which might say: "calculate the sum of the first 6 terms", we have to work out for ourselves what we have to do – especially in part (d): doesn't your heart sink when you have to form an equation yourself? Where do you start?

Answer: Part (a) is relatively straightforward. If Martha runs 2 hours extra each week then we have an arithmetic progression with common difference 2. It may help to scribble down the sequence to see what you're dealing with: 10, 12, 14 …. We are asked for the *total* number of hours spent running in the first 6 weeks, not just the number of hours in the sixth week itself. So we want the sum of the first 6 terms of the series. As I have mentioned already, always write down the formula you are going to use and then substitute the values in the next line.

Martha and David are training for a marathon.

a)   Martha runs for 10 hours in the first week. She then increases the time she spends running by 2 hours each week. Find the total number of hours she spends running during the first 6 weeks.

$$S_n = \frac{n}{2}(2u_1 + (n-1)d)$$

$$S_{12} = \frac{6}{2}(2 \times 10 + (6-1) \times 2)$$

$$= 3(20 + 10)$$

$$= \textbf{90 hours}$$

Part (b): We see that David "runs for 15% longer each week than the previous week." A 15% increase is equivalent to multiplying by 1.15, so if his time multiplies by 1.15 each week we can see that we are dealing with a geometric progression. Part (i) gives us a friendly "show that" so that we can see we're on the right track (note the "about" 13.2 hours – see my answer for how to tackle that). Part (ii) is the same as part (a) except with a geometric progression.

---

b)   David also runs for 10 hours in the first week. He then decided to run for 15% longer each week than in the previous week.

     i)   Show that in the third week he runs for about 13.2 hours.

$$u_n = u_1 r^{n-1}$$

$$u_3 = 10 \times 1.15^2$$

$$= 13.225$$

So he runs for about **13.2 hours** in week 3

---

     ii)   Find the total number of hours he spends running during the first 6 weeks.

$$S_n = \frac{u_1(r^n - 1)}{r - 1}$$

$$S_{12} = \frac{10(1.15^6 - 1)}{1.15 - 1}$$

$$= 87.54$$

So he runs about **88 hours** in 6 weeks

Part (c):   We have to be just a bit careful because we are asked in which week David runs more than 36 hours. We are looking for the first term in the series to exceed 36. If you solve this as an equation, you will find $n = 10.16$, so the temptation is to give the answer as 10 (by rounding down) – but in week 10 David only runs 35.17 hours; it's not until week 11 that he runs *more* than 36 hours. In these situations it is best to use an inequality.

c)	In which week will the time David spends running exceed 36 hours?

$$10 \times 1.15^{n-1} > 36$$

$$1.15^{n-1} > 3.6$$

$$n - 1 > \frac{\log 3.6}{\log 1.15}$$

$$n > 10.17$$

$$n = 11$$

David runs more than 36 hours in **week 11**

> Either use logs to solve equations where the unknown is a power, or use one of the various general equations solving methods on your GDC.

Part (d):   We can see from parts (a) and (b) that by week 6 Martha has run for more hours than David. But geometric progressions will always give higher totals eventually than arithmetic progressions, assuming a common ratio greater than 1. We need to find where "the lines will cross". So all we have to do is equate the total formula for Martha with the total formula for David, both of which we have already used, putting in the values for d, r and u_1. This will just leave n to be found, and this can only be done using a GDC (more on that in a later chapter).

d)	Form an equation in n, where n represents the number of weeks until they have completed the same total number of hours running. Solve for n to find in which week this occurs.

$$\frac{n}{2}(20 + (n-1) \times 2) = \frac{10(1.15^n - 1)}{1.15 - 1}$$

$$\frac{n}{2}(18 + 2n) = \frac{10(1.15^n - 1)}{0.15}$$

$$9n + n^2 = \frac{10(1.15^n - 1)}{0.15}$$

$$\frac{10(1.15^n - 1)}{0.15} - 9n - n^2 = 0$$

From GDC, $n = 7.593$, so they have the same total during week **8**

It looks a pretty awful equation, but this happens sometimes. And since it produced a very reasonable solution I'd go with it. If you have time to check, you could see what their totals were at the end of weeks 7 and 8. These come to:

Week 7:   Martha – 112 hours, David – 110.62 hours
Week 8:   Martha – 136 hours, David – 137.27 hours

You can clearly see the crossover in times which must have happened in week 8.

Question 11

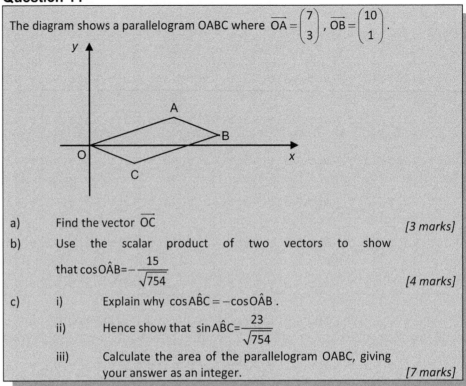

The diagram shows a parallelogram OABC where $\overrightarrow{OA} = \begin{pmatrix} 7 \\ 3 \end{pmatrix}$, $\overrightarrow{OB} = \begin{pmatrix} 10 \\ 1 \end{pmatrix}$.

a)   Find the vector $\overrightarrow{OC}$ *[3 marks]*

b)   Use the scalar product of two vectors to show

that $\cos O\hat{A}B = -\dfrac{15}{\sqrt{754}}$ *[4 marks]*

c)   i)   Explain why $\cos A\hat{B}C = -\cos O\hat{A}B$.

        ii)   Hence show that $\sin A\hat{B}C = \dfrac{23}{\sqrt{754}}$

       iii)   Calculate the area of the parallelogram OABC, giving your answer as an integer.   *[7 marks]*

Analysis: Clearly this question concerns vector geometry (syllabus sections 4.1 and 4.2), although it looks as if there is a possibility that we need the non-right angled triangle formulae. There's a new keyword: "explain". We need to be careful to do this properly – don't woffle on for several sentences, but think of a concise, clear answer in a sentence or two. We can also see a lot of connections between the parts: angle $O\hat{A}B$ appears in part (b), then again in (c)(i), whereas angle $A\hat{B}C$ appears in (c)(i) and (c)(ii), with a "hence" between them. The final part asks for the area of a parallelogram, presumably as a culmination of all the other parts – do we know how to find the area of a parallelogram?

Note too the surds, and in (c)(iii) the instruction to give our answer as an integer – although we can use our calculator in this question, we cannot give any answers as decimals.

Although this question looks as if it may present us with some difficulties, at least the mark allocation is not too scary (although 4 marks for part (b) implies there could be some numerical hurdles to jump). Another comforting feature is that in three of the five parts we are actually given the answer to work towards.

Answer:

In any parallelogram the vectors on opposite sides will always be equal.

Part (a): Straightforward bookwork – vector $\overrightarrow{AB}$ can be calculated as $\overrightarrow{OB} - \overrightarrow{OA}$, and $\overrightarrow{AB} = \overrightarrow{OC}$ since OABC is a parallelogram.

Part (b): Again, scalar (or dot) product is a standard bookwork topic. You should know how to find the angle between two vectors using the scalar product (although in this case we only have to go as far as the cosine of the angle). Be careful, though: you must always use vectors which are directed *away* from the angle. So for angle $O\hat{A}B$ you must use vectors $\overrightarrow{AO}$ and $\overrightarrow{AB}$; if you use $\overrightarrow{OA}$ you will not get the all-important minus sign in your answer.

The diagram shows a parallelogram OABC where $\overrightarrow{OA}=\begin{pmatrix}7\\3\end{pmatrix}$, $\overrightarrow{OB}=\begin{pmatrix}10\\1\end{pmatrix}$.

a)   Find the vector $\overrightarrow{OC}$

$$\overrightarrow{AB}=\overrightarrow{OB}-\overrightarrow{OA}=\begin{pmatrix}10\\1\end{pmatrix}-\begin{pmatrix}7\\3\end{pmatrix}=\begin{pmatrix}3\\-2\end{pmatrix}$$

Since OABC is a parallelogram, $\overrightarrow{OC}=\overrightarrow{AB}$

So, $\overrightarrow{OC}=\begin{pmatrix}3\\-2\end{pmatrix}$

b)   Use the scalar product of two vectors to show that $\cos O\hat{A}B=-\dfrac{15}{\sqrt{754}}$

$$\overrightarrow{AO}.\overrightarrow{AB}=\begin{pmatrix}-7\\-3\end{pmatrix}.\begin{pmatrix}3\\-2\end{pmatrix}=-21+6=-15$$

$$\cos O\hat{A}B=\frac{\overrightarrow{AO}.\overrightarrow{AB}}{|\overrightarrow{AO}||\overrightarrow{AB}|}=\frac{-15}{\sqrt{58}\sqrt{13}}=-\frac{15}{\sqrt{754}}\ \text{qed}$$

Since part (b) is worth 4 marks, I've put enough working in the answer to show exactly where the -15 and $\sqrt{754}$ come from.

Part (c):   So now we really do have to put our thinking caps on. First we have to explain why $\cos A\hat{B}C=-\cos O\hat{A}B$, so where do we begin? Clearly we have to identify the angles on the diagram and then see if we can see any connection between them. Have a look for yourself first. What jumps out at me is that they are adjacent interior angles of a parallelogram, and that means they must add to give 180° (make sure you know the various theorems for angles within parallel lines). So the question now becomes: "When two angles add to 180°, why is the cosine of one the negative cosine of the other?" I find the easiest way to work out this sort of relationship is to examine the graph of, in this case, $\cos\theta$.

Also worth knowing:
$\cos(\theta)=\cos(-\theta)$
$\sin(\theta)=-\sin(-\theta)$
$\sin(90-\theta)=\cos\theta$
$\cos(90-\theta)=\sin\theta$

I have indicated on the graph the angles 30° and 150° as examples, and it is clear from the symmetry that any two angles which add up to 180° will have cosines of x and $-x$. We now have an explanation for (c)(i).

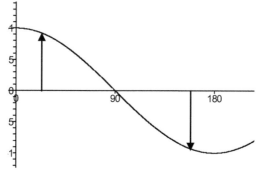

(c)(ii) has keyword "hence" and is a good example of how we need to look back at what we have already done. We want $\sin A\hat{B}C$; in the previous part we have a method for working out $\cos A\hat{B}C$; there must be a connection. And the connection is the identity $\sin^2\theta+\cos^2\theta=1$; in other words, we can always work out the sin from the cos, and vice versa.

(c)(iii): Now, there is a formula for the area of a parallelogram:
        Area = base × perpendicular height

but this doesn't seem relevant here. And since the question is labelled (iii) we can expect it to relate to (ii). The only area formula using the sin of an angle is for the general triangle ABC:

$$\text{Area} = \tfrac{1}{2}ab\sin C$$

Is this any use? If we were to use $\sin A\hat{B}C$ from part (ii) then we could find out the area of triangle ABC. Ah, there we are – the area of triangle ABC is half the area of the parallelogram. And this is a common technique in these questions requiring more thought: if you get stuck, don't necessarily think "how do I get the answer", but "what can I do with the things I've already worked out? What is their relevance?" But also note that if you couldn't work out (c)(i), say, you can still use the answer to continue with the rest of the question.

c)	i)	Explain why $\cos A\hat{B}C = -\cos O\hat{A}B$.

$A\hat{B}C + O\hat{A}B = 180°$ (interior angles of a parallelogram)

Thus $\cos A\hat{B}C = -\cos O\hat{A}B$

	ii)	Hence show that $\sin A\hat{B}C = \dfrac{23}{\sqrt{754}}$

$$\sin^2 A\hat{B}C + \cos^2 A\hat{B}C = 1$$

$$\sin^2 A\hat{B}C = 1 - \left(\frac{15}{\sqrt{754}}\right)^2$$

$$= 1 - \frac{225}{754}$$

$$= \frac{529}{754}$$

$$\text{Thus, } \sin ABC = \frac{23}{\sqrt{754}}$$

	iii)	Calculate the area of the parallelogram OABC, giving your answer as an integer.

Area of triangle ABC $= \tfrac{1}{2} \times BA \times BC \times \sin A\hat{B}C$

The lengths of BA and BC were found in part (b)

Thus, area of triangle ABC $= \tfrac{1}{2} \times \sqrt{13} \times \sqrt{58} \times \dfrac{23}{\sqrt{754}}$

$$= \tfrac{1}{2} \times 23$$

$$= 11.5$$

Area of parallelogram OABC = 2 × 11.5 = **23**

The fact that we used the lengths already calculated in part (b) indicates how important it is to show your working clearly – not just for the examiner, but for you as well!

Question 12

> The function f is given by $f(x) = ax^3 + bx^2 + cx$ where a, b, and c are integers. The tangent to the graph of f at the point where $x = 0$ is parallel to the line $2x + y = 3$.
>
> a)   Show that $c = -2$.   [3 marks]
>
> The graph of f also passes through the points (2, 24) and (-1, 0)
>
> b)   Write down two equations in a, b and c.   [2 marks]
>
> c)   Use the results of parts (a) and (b) to calculate the values of a and b.   [4 marks]
>
> d)   The function f can also be written as $f(x) = x(x - p)(qx - r)$ where p, q, and r are integers. Find p, q, and r.   [4 marks]

Analysis: Keywords: *Show, write down, find*; nothing unusual there. But there seem to be a lot of bits and pieces in the question. We start with a cubic function (expect to have to find the values of a, b and c; but then we are straight into tangents – this often involves differentiation, but there is no mention of $f'(x)$ as there has been in questions so far. In part (c) we have to calculate two unknowns – surely that will be simultaneous equations? You may remember that in question 2 we had a situation where a quadratic function was given to us with letters instead of numbers, and we had to work out their values. My advice there was to see whether there were some points to substitute, and here we have exactly the same situation again in part (b) – although this time we have to do two separate substitutions to get two equations.

What has part (d) got to do with the other parts? Factorisation of quadratic functions is a familiar part of the syllabus: in this case, we are being asked to factorise a cubic function. See if you can work out how to do it in this case before I show you in the answers.

Answer:

Part (a):   Let's walk through this question logically. If a tangent is parallel to a line that means they have the same gradient. So, find the gradient of the graph at the point where $x = 0$ (this will require some differentiation) and also find the gradient of the given line. By putting them equal to each other we would hope to find the value of c. As ever, because it is a *show that* question, we must give clear working.

Part (b):   Now we need to substitute the coordinates of the two points for x and $f(x)$, but let's be careful (as always) when substituting a negative value. If $x = -2$, what is the value of x^2? Yes, it's 4. Now work that out on your calculator: if you get -4 you must have done something wrong. The answer is that you *must* put negative numbers into brackets on your calculator to ensure correct calculations. I've been very cautious with the working, especially for the second equation, but it never hurts to show what you have done.

> The function f is given by $f(x) = ax^3 + bx^2 + cx$ where a, b and c are integers. The tangent to the graph of f at the point where $x = 0$ is parallel to the line $2x + y = 3$.
>
> a)   Show that $c = -2$
>
> $f'(x) = 3ax^2 + 2bx + c$
>
> When $x = 0$, $f'(x) = c$
>
> The line $2x + y = 3$ can be rewritten as $y = -2x + 3$, and therefore has gradient = -2.
>
> Thus $c = -2$, *q.e.d.*

b)	Write down two equations in a, b, and c.

Substitute $x = 2$, $f(x) = 24$

$$24 = a \times 2^3 + b \times 2^2 + c \times 2$$

So, **$8a + 4b + 2c = 24$**

Substitute $x = -1$, $f(x) = 0$

$$0 = a \times (-1)^3 + b \times (-1)^2 + c \times (-1)$$

So, **$-a + b - c = 0$**

Part (c):   So, what do we now know? We have the value of c, and we have two equations in three unknowns – that's a bit unusual. But since we know c we can substitute the value into the two equations, and we will end up with a standard pair of simultaneous equations. If this was a Paper 2 question we could use our GDC to solve the equations; if not we can either use elimination or substitution: I've chosen elimination because the form of the equations lends itself to this method.

c)	Use the results of parts (a) and (b) to calculate the values of a and b.

Substituting $c = -2$ we get:

$$8a + 4b - 4 = 24$$
$$-a + b + 2 = 0$$

Simplifying and rearranging gives:

$$2a + b = 7$$
$$-a + b = -2$$

Subtract the second equation from the first:

$$3a = 9, \text{ so } \mathbf{a = 3}$$

Substitute this value into the second equation (easier numbers than the first)!

$$-3 + b = -2, \text{ so } \mathbf{b = 1}$$

Part (d):   Having worked through several parts of long questions, it's then easy to forget what you are doing and what is the implication of your answer. Try to keep an overview of the whole question. So, here we started with a cubic function, but we didn't know the values of the coefficients in each term. But now we do know them, having calculated the values of a, b and c. Part (d) is now asking us to rewrite the function in factorised form. Do we know how to factorise a cubic? Not generally, no, but because there is no constant term we can take out x as a common factor – and that just leaves a quadratic to factorise. Note that it is conventional to write a factor as, say, $(x - a)$ even if the factor has a plus sign it – e.g. $(x + 3)$. It just means that value of a will be negative; in this case, $a = -3$.

d)	The function f can also be written as $f(x) = x(x - p)(qx - r)$ where p, q and r are integers. Find p, q and r.

Substituting the values of a, b and c we get:

$$f(x) = 3x^3 + x^2 - 2x$$
$$= x(3x^2 + x - 2)$$
$$= x(3x - 2)(x + 1)$$

Thus **$p = -1$, $q = 3$, $r = 2$**

Now it's over to you again. Don't forget that in each of the following practice questions there will be at least one part where you have to spend some time either working out just what the question is asking you to do, or what techniques you need to find the answer. Sometimes it helps to read on (if there are further parts to the question): there may just be a clue there; or try to work out logically how the different parts of the question relate to each other. Don't look at the hints and answers unless you really have to – they won't be there when you take the exam for real!

Question 13

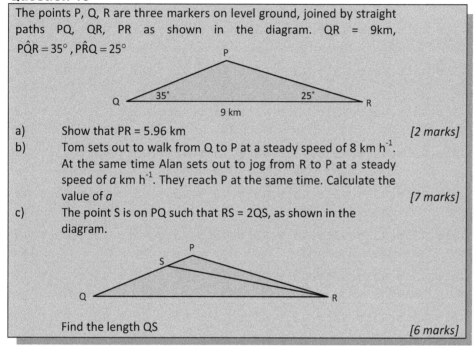

The points P, Q, R are three markers on level ground, joined by straight paths PQ, QR, PR as shown in the diagram. QR = 9km, $P\hat{Q}R = 35°$, $P\hat{R}Q = 25°$

a)   Show that PR = 5.96 km   [2 marks]

b)   Tom sets out to walk from Q to P at a steady speed of 8 km h⁻¹. At the same time Alan sets out to jog from R to P at a steady speed of a km h⁻¹. They reach P at the same time. Calculate the value of a [7 marks]

c)   The point S is on PQ such that RS = 2QS, as shown in the diagram.

Find the length QS   [6 marks]

Hints: Part (a) is a straightforward sine rule (how do I know it isn't cosine rule)? Part (b) involves time, distance and constant speed, for which the relationship is distance = speed × time. There are 7 marks because you have to start by forming your own equation. Part (c) is really quite stretching – there is very little help given to you. My instinct would be to look at triangle QRS since RS and QS are both in this triangle, and we also know angle Q and length QR.

(b)   The key to this question is that both Tom and Alan set out at the same time and finish at the same time: this forms the basis of an equation. Work out how long Tom takes using speed and distance – you will need to find the distance QP. Then find an expression for the time that Alan takes which will involve a. Then put them equal to each other.

(c)   The only angle we know is Q. We know the length QR, and we are interested in the lengths QS and SR, so it looks like the cosine rule. But we don't know *either* of QS or SR – however, we *do* know that SR is double the length of QS. In this sort of situation, call one of them x and the other $2x$, substitute all the information into the formula (the cosine rule in this case) and see what happens. Hopefully you will end up with an equation in x to solve.

You'll find it helpful to redraw triangle RSQ (make it nice and big) and then fill in the 9, the 35°, the x and the $2x$.

Answers:

(a) $PR = \dfrac{9\sin 35°}{\sin 120°}$

(b)   PQ = 4.39 km

$\dfrac{4.39}{8} = \dfrac{5.96}{a} \Rightarrow a = 10.9\,\text{kmh}^{-1}$

(c) $(2x)^2 = x^2 + 81 - 18x\cos 35°$ (where x = QS)

QS = 3.29 km

Question 14

Bag A contains 3 red balls and 4 blue balls. Bag B contains 5 red balls and 3 blue balls. Two balls are selected at random from bag A

a)   i)   Show that P(2 red balls) = $\dfrac{1}{7}$

       ii)   Find P(1 ball of each colour)   *[4 marks]*

John selects one of the bags by throwing a standard die with 6 faces. If he throws a 1 or a 6 he selects bag A; otherwise he selects bag B. Then he takes out two balls from the chosen bag.

b)   Calculate the probability that he draws out 2 red balls.   *[4 marks]*

c)   Find the probability that John selected bag A given that he drew out 2 red balls   *[4 marks]*

John carries out the same trial 42 times.

d)   On how many occasions would he expect to draw two red balls?   *[2 marks]*

Tree diagrams are used to help calculate the probability of events which happen sequentially; at each stage the branches represent all the possible outcomes..

Hints: This is a fairly standard probability situation complicated by the selection of the bags in part (b). With many probability problems, part of the secret is to say, in simple words, what is actually happening. In this case: "First choose either bag A or bag B; then select two balls from the chosen bag." Put like that it should then become fairly obvious that we need a tree diagram. Once again the "given that" in part (c) tells us to put our conditional probability hats on. You should be able to do this question without a calculator – brush up your fractions!

(a)   (i)   This is selection without replacement – in other words, once one red ball has been selected, the probability of another red ball will be different.

       (ii)   Your tree diagram should show you that there are two possible ways of drawing out one ball of each colour.

(b)   Your routes through the enlarged tree diagram will be:
       Bag A and first red ball and second red ball
          OR
       Bag B and first red ball and second red ball.

(c)   Conditional probability from a tree diagram is easy. Suppose I wake up late 1 day out of 5. If I wake up late I miss the bus 50% of the time, otherwise I miss the bus 10% of the time.

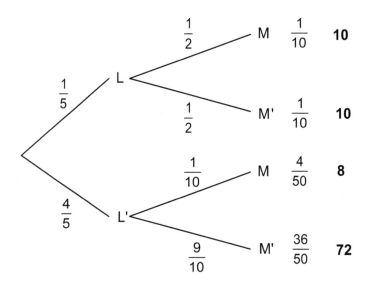

Remember that all the branches coming out from any single point on a tree diagram *must* represent all the possibilities at that point.

I've put all the probabilities on a tree diagram and also the number of times each outcome would be expected to occur in 100 days (in other words, there would be 8 occasions in 100 when I wouldn't wake up late but I would miss the bus). Given that I miss the bus, what is the probability that I woke up late? Well, I missed the bus 18 times, and I woke up late on 10 of those occasions, so $P(L|M) = \dfrac{10}{18} = \dfrac{5}{9}$; or, using

I chose 100 simply because it was a simple number by which to multiply each of the fractions.

the probabilities, $\dfrac{\frac{1}{10}}{\frac{1}{10}+\frac{4}{50}} = \dfrac{\frac{5}{50}}{\frac{9}{50}} = \dfrac{5}{9}$. This, of course, reflects the formula for

conditional probability: $P(A|B) = \dfrac{P(A \cap B)}{P(B)}$

(d)   The expected mean of an event is calculated as probability of success × number of trials.

Answers:

(a)   (i) $P(2 \text{ red balls}) = \dfrac{3}{7} \times \dfrac{2}{6}$ (ii) $\dfrac{4}{7}$

(b) $\dfrac{6}{21}$

(c) $\dfrac{1}{6}$

(d)   12

Question 15

The diagram shows the graphs of $f(x) = \dfrac{1}{x}$, $g(x) = x - 2$, $x > 0$. The graphs intersect where $x = a$.

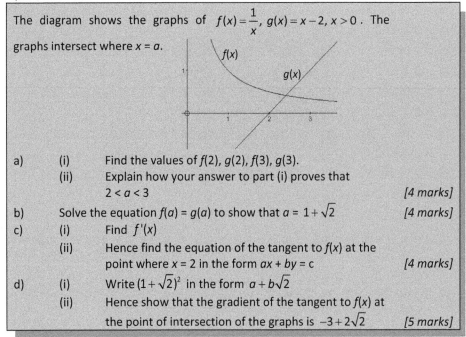

a)   (i)   Find the values of $f(2), g(2), f(3), g(3)$.

       (ii)   Explain how your answer to part (i) proves that
             $2 < a < 3$ *[4 marks]*

b)   Solve the equation $f(a) = g(a)$ to show that $a = 1 + \sqrt{2}$ *[4 marks]*

c)   (i)   Find $f'(x)$

       (ii)   Hence find the equation of the tangent to $f(x)$ at the
             point where $x = 2$ in the form $ax + by = c$ *[4 marks]*

d)   (i)   Write $(1 + \sqrt{2})^2$ in the form $a + b\sqrt{2}$

       (ii)   Hence show that the gradient of the tangent to $f(x)$ at
             the point of intersection of the graphs is $-3 + 2\sqrt{2}$ *[5 marks]*

Surds: you should be able to
- Appreciate:
  $$\sqrt{a} \times \sqrt{b} = \sqrt{ab}$$
  $$\frac{\sqrt{a}}{\sqrt{b}} = \sqrt{\frac{a}{b}}$$
- Rationalise:
  $$\frac{a}{\sqrt{b}}, \ \frac{a}{b + \sqrt{c}} \text{ etc}$$
- Calculate:
  $$(a + \sqrt{b})(c + \sqrt{d})$$

To find the equation of a straight line, either start with $y = mx + c$, find m, then substitute a point to find c; or, use $y - y_1 = m(x - x_1)$ substitute m and a point, then simplify the answer.

Hints: Look through the question: there's differentiation, and talk of tangents and gradients, which all makes sense. But surds also feature prominently – where did *they* come from. Part (b) gives us a clue: we have to solve an equation and there's a square root in the answer. That suggests to me the possibility of a quadratic. There's also quite a variety of key words. By now, you should know how to deal with the "hences"; there's a "show", and also the dreaded "explain". Do try and make your reasoning simple, clear and fairly short. Use the diagram – perhaps make a large copy for yourself. And add things to it as the question progresses.

(a)   (ii)   To the left of the point of intersection $f(x) > g(x)$. The opposite is true to the right of the point of intersection.

(b)   Quadratic equation – rearrange as $h(a) = 0$. Since $x > 0$ (see the domain of the functions) you will only get one solution.

(c)   (i)   Before differentiating, rewrite $f(x)$ using a negative power of x.

       (ii)   Make sure your answer is in the specified format.

(d)   You really need to be familiar with the manipulation of surds to get anywhere in this part. This is a non-calculator question.

Answers:

(a)   (i) $0.5, 0, 0.\dot{3}, 1$

       (ii) $f(2) > g(2)$, but $f(3) < g(3)$, so the graphs must intersect between $x = 2$ and $x = 3$. Hence $2 < a < 3$

(b)   The equation is $a^2 - 2a - 1 = 0$.

(c)   (i) $f'(x) = -\dfrac{1}{x^2}$

       (ii) $x + 4y = 1$

(d)   (i) $3 + 2\sqrt{2}$

       (ii)   The gradient is $-\dfrac{1}{3 + 2\sqrt{2}}$. This has to be rationalised.

Question 16

Two standard six-sided dice are tossed. If X represents the difference between the two scores then the following table represents the sample space for X.

Score on second die

		1	2	3	4	5	6
	1	0	1	2	3	4	5
	2	1	0	1	2	3	4
Score on first die	3	2	1	0	1	2	3
	4	3	2	1	0	1	2
	5	4	3	2	1	0	1
	6	5	4	3	2	1	0

a) Find
   (i) $P(X = 3)$
   (ii) $P(X > 3)$
   (iii) The probability that one of the dice shows a 3 given that the difference between the scores is 1. *[6 marks]*

b) Show that the expected mean $E(X)$ is just under 2. *[3 marks]*

c) A game is devised where the two dice are tossed and points scored depending on the difference in the scores.
   If the difference is 1,2, or 3 then 2 points are scored.
   If the difference is 4 or 5 then 4 points are scored.
   If the difference is 0 then k points are **lost**.
   Find the value of k such that the expected number of points is zero. *[5 marks]*

Hints: This is a question about probability distributions (syllabus section 6.9). The possible outcomes are 0, 1, 2, 3, 4, 5 and you will need to calculate the probability of each of those outcomes – that is the key to the whole question. "Expected value" features in both parts (b) and (c); the expected value (or expected mean or expectation) is calculated by multiplying each possible outcome by the probability of that outcome occurring, and adding all the products together.

(a) (iii)   Conditional probability again, but very easily worked out by looking at the diagram. How many ways can you get a difference of 1? And out of those outcomes, how many involved a 3 on either die?

(b) Show the calculation of the expected mean (use fractions – this is a non-calculator question), and the result should be just less than 2.

(c) We now have to reverse part (b). We *know* that the expected mean is 0: set up an equation involving k and solve it.

Answers:

(a) (i) $\dfrac{1}{6}$;   (ii) $\dfrac{1}{6}$;   (iii) $\dfrac{2}{5}$

(b) $\dfrac{6}{36} \times 0 + \dfrac{10}{36} \times 1 + \dfrac{8}{36} \times 2 + \dfrac{6}{36} \times 3 + \dfrac{4}{36} \times 4 + \dfrac{2}{36} \times 5 = \dfrac{35}{18} = 1\dfrac{17}{18}$

(c) Expected mean = $\dfrac{24}{36} \times 2 + \dfrac{6}{36} \times 4 - \dfrac{6}{36} \times k = 0$

   $k = 12$

Note the minus sign in part (c). If you used a plus sign you would end up with $k = -12$; it wouldn't matter too much as long as you showed the working clearly and interpreted your answer.

Question 17

The points A and B have position vectors $\begin{pmatrix} 2 \\ -2 \end{pmatrix}$ and $\begin{pmatrix} -1 \\ -1 \end{pmatrix}$ respectively.

a)   (i)   Find the vector $\overrightarrow{AB}$

         (ii)   Find $\left|\overrightarrow{AB}\right|$

[3 marks]

The point D has position vector $\begin{pmatrix} d \\ 4 \end{pmatrix}$

b)   Find the vector $\overrightarrow{AD}$ in terms of d.   *[2 marks]*

The angle $B\hat{A}D$ is $90°$

c)   (i)   Show that $d = 4$

         (ii)   Write down the position vector of the point D   *[3 marks]*

The quadrilateral ABCD is a rectangle

d)   Find the position vector of the point C   *[3 marks]*

e)   Find the area of rectangle ABCD.   *[3 marks]*

Hints: You will find it very hard to do this question, and similar vector geometry questions, without a diagram. It doesn't have to be accurate – just a sketch showing roughly where the points are. And, as you build up information in each part, add it to your diagram. Make your diagram nice and big and try to keep an overview of everything that's happening as you work through the question. It is almost always the case with vector geometry questions that the parts are strongly linked to each other.

(a)   (ii)   The symbol means the length of the vector.

(c)   (i)   If you know your vector geometry syllabus (sections 5.1 to 5.4) you'll recall that the scalar product of two perpendicular vectors is 0.

(d)   If ABCD is a rectangle then $\overrightarrow{BC} = \overrightarrow{AD}$. You know what $\overrightarrow{AD}$ is so you can easily find C.

(e)   In part (a) you find the length AB. Now find the length of BC (or AD, which is the same) and you can calculate the area of the rectangle. This is a non-calculator question, so you will need to use surd algebra.

Answers:

(a)   (i) $\begin{pmatrix} -3 \\ 1 \end{pmatrix}$;   (ii) $\sqrt{10}$

(b) $\begin{pmatrix} d-2 \\ 6 \end{pmatrix}$

(c)   (i) $\begin{pmatrix} -3 \\ 1 \end{pmatrix} \cdot \begin{pmatrix} d-2 \\ 6 \end{pmatrix} = 0 \Rightarrow -3d + 6 + 6 = 0 \Rightarrow d = 4$

      (ii) $\begin{pmatrix} 4 \\ 4 \end{pmatrix}$

(d) $\begin{pmatrix} 1 \\ 5 \end{pmatrix}$

(e)   20

QUESTIONS WITH HARDER ALGEBRA

In the first two chapters we have been looking at how you should be thinking through questions. But I have deliberately chosen questions where the algebra hasn't been too hard. In this chapter we shall consider techniques for coping with questions which require you to use algebra at a higher level. It can be frustrating if you know how to do a question, but you can't get to the answer because the algebra defeats you.

Where is the harder algebra likely to be found in a question? Very often you may find yourself solving a nasty looking equation, and this may itself have come from a graphing question; composite functions; a complex piece of geometry; use of trigonometric formulae. Or a calculus question may require you to differentiate a function, say, by the product rule, and then simplify the answer. Even finding an inverse function can sometimes be quite taxing. In other words, there are a variety of situations where you find you need to be pretty good at algebra – familiar with techniques, and able to manipulate accurately.

But you can make mistakes with simple algebra as well. The most common situations where people go wrong involve algebraic fractions, minus signs, and brackets. It is not within the scope of this book to provide an algebra course, but have a look at the following examples – they each involve an elementary mistake (which of course *you* wouldn't make, would you?)

(a)	$\dfrac{3x^2+5}{2x} = \dfrac{3x+5}{2}$	(b)	$3-2(x+1)=3-2x+2=5-2x$
(c)	$(3x)^2 = 3x^2$	(d)	$(x+2)^2 = x^2+4$
(e)	$\dfrac{6}{x+2} = \dfrac{6}{x}+3$	(f)	$\dfrac{1}{3x^2} = 3x^{-2}$

It's quite hard to give specific advice since there are so many difficulties which can present themselves. But in general, work methodically, check everything you do carefully, and *always* beware of minus signs and the havoc they can wreak!

One specific area of difficulty is when you are asked to form an equation from information you have been given. For example:

The area under the graph of $y = x^2 - 2$ between $x = 1$ and $x = a$ is $1\frac{1}{3}$. Find the value of a.

How can you do a definite integral when you aren't given both the limits numerically? The answer, in this and dozens of similar situations, is to treat a as the number it actually is, and carry on as normal. You may not know what's going to happen as you work through the question, but just get going and see.

$$\int_1^a x^2 - 2\,dx = 1\tfrac{1}{3}$$

$$\left[\tfrac{1}{3}x^3 - 2x\right]_1^a = 1\tfrac{1}{3}$$

$$(\tfrac{1}{3}a^3 - 2a) - (\tfrac{1}{3} - 2) = 1\tfrac{1}{3}$$

We now have an equation to solve, and the GDC gives us $a = 3$.

Question 18

(a)   Let $y = -16x^2 + 160x - 256$. Given that y has a maximum value,
find: (i)   the value of x giving the maximum value of y;
         (ii)   this maximum value of y.   *[4 marks]*

The triangle XYZ has XZ = 6, YZ = x, XY = z as shown below. The perimeter of the triangle is 16.

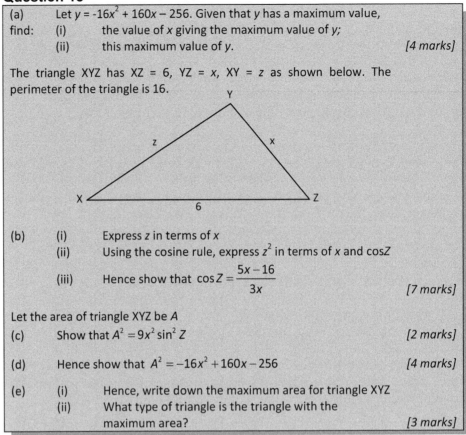

(b)   (i)   Express z in terms of x
         (ii)   Using the cosine rule, express z^2 in terms of x and $\cos Z$
         (iii)   Hence show that $\cos Z = \dfrac{5x - 16}{3x}$ *[7 marks]*

Let the area of triangle XYZ be A

(c)   Show that $A^2 = 9x^2 \sin^2 Z$ *[2 marks]*

(d)   Hence show that $A^2 = -16x^2 + 160x - 256$ *[4 marks]*

(e)   (i)   Hence, write down the maximum area for triangle XYZ
         (ii)   What type of triangle is the triangle with the maximum area?   *[3 marks]*

Analysis: Well, there's enough here to make your heart sink, isn't there? Part (a) looks fairly straightforward: finding a maximum implies we're going to be differentiating. But then in part (b) we are into the cosine rule – there doesn't seem to be any connection with part (a) at all. In part (iii) we've got a *hence*, so presumably we're going to be rearranging the formula we found in part (ii) – but that had a z in it, and z doesn't appear in part (iii). Let's hope that becomes clearer when we actually do the algebra.

Then in part (c), things get worse – when have we ever come across the *square* of the area before? But we do know the general formula for the area of a triangle, so let's assume we're going to be using that. But, wait, that expression in part (d) is the same as in part (a), so presumably we're now going to use that maximum we found. Yes, (e)(i) mentions the maximum again. And in (e)(ii) we're asked for a type of triangle: since the only special triangles we know about are right-angled, isosceles and equilateral, the answer must be one of those. A one in three chance of getting that one right, then!

Overall, this is pretty typical of the harder algebra type of question where you don't really know what's going to happen until you try it. In many of the questions we have tackled so far, we've been able to see our path through the question before we start. Not here, so we must tackle each part methodically, always with an eye on previous parts to see if the working we have already done is relevant.

Answers:
Part (a):   Why the phrase: "Given that y has a maximum value..."? Because in questions involving turning points you usually have to decide whether or a turning point is a maximum or a minimum – not here, because you are told it is a maximum.

This part of the question is EASY – so don't waste marks by getting it wrong (for example, by ignoring the minus sign at the beginning, or by miscalculating the value of *y*). Without too much effort you will have 4 marks in the bag.

(a)	Let $y = -16x^2 + 160x - 256$. Given that *y* has a maximum value, find:
(i)	the value of *x* giving the maximum value of *y*;
(ii)	this maximum value of *y*.

(i) $\dfrac{dy}{dx} = -32x + 160$

For a turning point, -32*x* + 160 = 0, so **x = 5**

(ii)   When *x* = 5, $y = -16 \times 5^2 + 160 \times 5 - 256$
                = 144

So the maximum value of *y* is **144**

Right back in question 1 I mentioned that it is a good idea to show the substitution you are doing before working it out – it really does help put your brain in gear, and you are more likely to end up with the correct answer.

Part (b): (i) Sometimes you can stare at even the simplest question for ages without seeing the light. If you are wondering how to express *z* in terms of *x* (can't be sine or cosine rule because you haven't got any angles) then it's because you haven't read the question. ALWAYS read the information given in the introduction to a question; don't skim over words and sentences without taking them in. In this case, we are told that the perimeter of the triangle is 16. If two of the sides are *z* and *x*, and the third side is 6…….

In part (ii) we simply have to apply the cosine rule. And probably the method for part (iii) will become apparent once we have the answers to (i) and (ii) – let's do those first.

> The sine rule, cosine rule and area of a triangle formula all appear in your information book.

The triangle XYZ has XZ = 6, YZ = *x*, XY = *z* as shown below. The perimeter of the triangle is 16.		
(b)	(i)	Express *z* in terms of *x*
		x + *z* + 6 = 16, so **z = 10 – x**

	(ii)	Using the cosine rule, express z^2 in terms of *x* and cos*Z*
		$z^2 = x^2 + 36 - 2.x.6.\cos Z$
		$z^2 = x^2 + 36 - 12x\cos Z$

Part (b) (iii): Look carefully at the question. We want to express cos*Z* just in terms of *x*. We could rearrange the answer to part (ii) to make cos*Z* the subject, but there would be a *z* in the expression as well. Ah, but in (i) we have seen that we can replace *z* with 10 – *x*, so that should get us to the required answer. Let's try it out – but before you look at my working on the next page I think it would be a good idea for you to try and work through to the answer yourself.

(iii)	Hence show that $\cos Z = \dfrac{5x-16}{3x}$

(1) $12x\cos Z = x^2 + 36 - z^2$

(2) $12x\cos Z = x^2 + 36 - (10-x)^2$

(3) $12x\cos Z = x^2 + 36 - (100 - 20x + x^2)$

(4) $12x\cos Z = x^2 + 36 - 100 + 20x - x^2$

(5) $12x\cos Z = 20x - 64$

(6) $\cos Z = \dfrac{20x - 64}{12x}$

(7) $\cos Z = \dfrac{5x - 16}{3x}$

There are some points about the algebra I want to make here, so I've numbered the lines.

Line (1): A rearrangement of the formula in (b)(ii).

Line (2): Substitute $z = 10 - x$, but I've used brackets. Whenever you substitute a negative number, or an expression, for a single letter, it is a good move to use brackets. Especially here where there is a minus sign in front.

Line (3): I've multiplied out the brackets.

Line (4): I've removed the brackets, taking account of the minus sign.

Line (5): Simplification – always simplify algebra before moving on.

Line (6): $\cos Z$ has been made the subject – I didn't do it earlier because I wanted to avoid having a denominator for as long as possible.

Line (7): The numerator and denominator have been divided through by 4.

Now, you may in practice leave out some of those lines of working when you write your answer in an exam – but it would be *very* sensible to try it all out in rough first. You may well make a mistake (I did when I worked it through for the first time: it was rather late at night and I wrote $2x$ instead of $20x$ in line 3) and it really doesn't help the examiner if your answers have more crossings out than actual work.

How far did you get ? If you made a mistake in the algebra and couldn't see why, do try and learn from it – otherwise you'll just make the same mistake next time.

Part (c) looks a bit nasty, but with only 2 marks it can't be hard. We *must* use the area of a triangle formula and then, presumably, we just square the result. Let's try that, anyway.

Let the area of triangle XYZ be A

(c)   Show that $A^2 = 9x^2 \sin^2 Z$

$$\text{Area} = \tfrac{1}{2}ab\sin C$$
$$= \tfrac{1}{2} \times 6 \times x \times \sin Z$$
$$= 3x\sin Z$$
$$\text{So, } A^2 = 9x^2\sin^2 Z$$

Part (d):   This begins with a *hence*. Part (c) ends up with a formula for A^2 in terms of x and $\sin Z$. But we want a formula for A^2 just in terms of x. How can we dispose of the $\sin Z$? Looking back through our answers the only clue we have is in (b)(iii) where we ended up with a formula for $\cos Z$. Is there a connection? Yes: $\sin^2 Z + \cos^2 Z = 1$. So, working logically:

- Rewrite the trigonometric formula to give $\sin^2 Z$ in terms of $\cos^2 Z$
- Now rewrite $\sin^2 Z$ in terms of x (using (b)(iii))
- Now rewrite A^2 in terms of x.

(d)	Hence show that $A^2 = -16x^2 + 160x - 256$

$$\sin^2 Z = 1 - \cos^2 Z$$

So, $A^2 = 9x^2 \sin^2 Z$

$$= 9x^2(1 - \cos^2 Z)$$

$$= 9x^2\left(1 - \left(\frac{5x-16}{3x}\right)^2\right)$$

$$= 9x^2\left(1 - \left(\frac{25x^2 - 160x + 256}{9x^2}\right)\right)$$

$$= 9x^2\left(\frac{9x^2 - 25x^2 + 160x - 256}{9x^2}\right)$$

$$= -16x^2 + 160x - 256$$

The algebra in there isn't easy. I've taken it slowly and carefully, ensuring that I use brackets for substitutions and looking out for minus signs. I suggest that you work through it until you really understand the algebraic manipulation involved, and then try it yourself a couple of times. The principles are well worth grasping fully.

Note part (e) relates directly to part (a). Are we looking for the value of x or the value of y? The value of y equates to the area, so that's what we want.

(e)	(i)	Hence, write down the maximum area for triangle XYZ

The maximum area is 12

	(ii)	What type of triangle is the triangle with the maximum area?

The area is a maximum when $x = 5$.
Since $z = 10 - x$, $z = 5$ as well
So the triangle is isosceles

Question 19

Let $f(x) = m - \dfrac{3x}{x^2 - n^2}$, where $m, n \in \mathbb{R}^+$

Part of the graph of f, including the asymptotes, is shown below

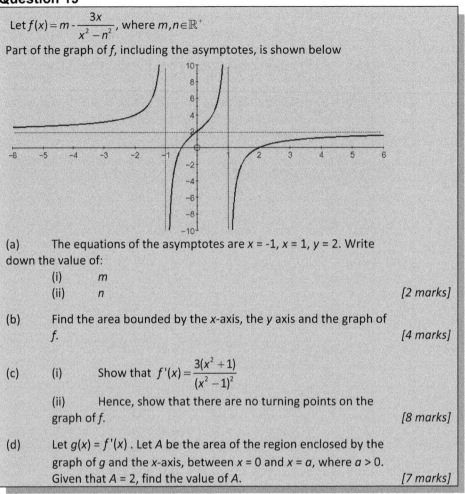

(a)   The equations of the asymptotes are $x = -1$, $x = 1$, $y = 2$. Write down the value of:

        (i) m

        (ii) n *[2 marks]*

(b)   Find the area bounded by the x-axis, the y axis and the graph of f.   *[4 marks]*

(c)   (i)   Show that $f'(x) = \dfrac{3(x^2 + 1)}{(x^2 - 1)^2}$

        (ii)   Hence, show that there are no turning points on the graph of f.   *[8 marks]*

(d)   Let $g(x) = f'(x)$. Let A be the area of the region enclosed by the graph of g and the x-axis, between $x = 0$ and $x = a$, where $a > 0$. Given that $A = 2$, find the value of A.   *[7 marks]*

Analysis: Looking through the question we can see that every part relates to the graph (although part (d) refers to the graph of $g(x)$). It's not a straightforward graph, so let's have a look at its main features. Most obviously there are two vertical asymptotes – these arise solely from values of x which involve division by zero. For example, a factor of $(x - 4)$ in the denominator will lead to a vertical asymptote of $x = 4$. The horizontal asymptote on a graph can be found by considering what happens as x gets very large. For example, consider the function $f(x) = \dfrac{2x - 3}{x + 1}$. For very large values of x the fraction is very close to 2; the larger x gets, the closer the fraction tends towards 2. So the horizontal asymptote of the graph of $f(x)$ is $y = 2$.

> Using your calculator, work out the values of $f(10)$, $f(100)$ and $f(1000)$.

We also note that the graph intersects the x-axis at two points, and that the gradient is always positive (that is, the values of y are always increasing). This means that there are no turning points, a fact we have to prove in part (c).

The letters m and n appear in the function: we've seen that this probably means we're going to have to work them out and, sure enough, that's the first question. Have a look at the denominator of $f'(x)$ in part (c) – does this suggest what the value of n might be?

Both parts (b) and (d) involve the area under the curve, so we're in integration territory. (d) looks particularly complicated to understand, so we'll spend some time looking at that. Marks? Parts (c) and (d) have 15 marks between them, so expect some algebraic fireworks!

Answer: Part (a): Note the keyword *write down*. The value of n is straightforward and is derived from the vertical asymptotes. For the horizontal asymptote, consider the function $h(x) = 4 + \dfrac{1}{x+3}$. As x gets very large the fraction part of the function gets closer to zero, so the value of the whole function is tending towards 4. Thus the horizontal asymptote is $y = 4$. In our function something similar is happening. The fractional part of the function is $\dfrac{3x}{x^2 - n^2}$ which tends towards zero as x gets large, whatever the value of n. So we can work out m if we know the horizontal asymptote – which we do!

Let $f(x) = m - \dfrac{3x}{x^2 - n^2}$, where $m, n \in \mathbb{R}^+$

(a) The equations of the asymptotes are $x = -1$, $x = 1$, $y = 2$. Write down the value of:

    (i) m

    (ii) n

             $m = 2$, $n = 1$

With the values of m and n, we can now write down the function as $f(x) = 2 - \dfrac{3x}{x^2 - 1}$. In part (b) we are going to have to integrate this to find the area under the curve. This integration is beyond the scope of the SL course, so we must use the GDC. So why are there 4 marks? Because we don't know both the limits of the definite integral. Look at the graph again, and identify the area we are going to calculate: there is only one region enclosed by the graph and the x- and y- axes. The upper limit is clearly $x = 0$, but the lower limit is where the graph first intersects the x-axis. We could find this by solving the equation $2 - \dfrac{3x}{x^2 - 1} = 0$ (this is a quadratic equation, and that fits because there are two points where the graph intersects the x-axis), but since this is a calculator question we can also use the GDC to solve the equation.

Graphs and your GDC

You should be able to:
- Set a sensible window to view the graph
- Find the zeroes
- Find where two graphs intersect
- Find the gradient at any point
- Find the area under the graph between two points

(b) Find the area bounded by the x-axis, the y axis and the graph of f.

The graph intersects the x-axis where $2 - \dfrac{3x}{x^2 - 1} = 0$

The solution between -1 and 0 is $x = -0.5$ (GDC)

$\therefore$ The required area is $\displaystyle\int_{-0.5}^{0} 2 - \dfrac{3x}{x^2 - 1}\,dx$ = **0.568** (GDC)

As I mentioned before, when using your GDC for anything other than simple calculations, make sure you show enough working so that the examiner knows you understand how to answer the question.

In part (c) we must differentiate $f(x)$. For the fraction we must use the quotient rule, and then we must simplify the algebra so that we end up with the answer in the same form as required by the question: again, the marks here are for the working – make it nice and clear. How do we then use this to show there are no turning points? For a turning point, $f'(x) = 0$, so we must show that there are no solutions to that equation.

(c)   (i)   Show that $f'(x) = \dfrac{3(x^2+1)}{(x^2-1)^2}$

$$f(x) = 2 - \frac{3x}{x^2-1}$$

$$f'(x) = -\frac{(x^2-1).3 - 3x.2x}{(x^2-1)^2}$$

$$= -\frac{3x^2 - 3 - 6x^2}{(x^2-1)^2}$$

$$= -\frac{-3x^2 - 3}{(x^2-1)^2}$$

$$= \frac{3(x^2+1)}{(x^2-1)^2}$$

    (ii)   Hence, show that there are no turning points on the graph of f.

For a turning point $f'(x) = 0$
So $3(x^2 + 1) = 0 \Rightarrow x^2 = -1$
There are no solutions to this equation, so there are no turning points on the graph

A few points about the algebra in (i).

- I have used dots instead of multiplication signs – it is easier to follow (but only do this when they cannot be mistaken for decimal points).
- In the final line of working the minus sign in front of the fraction has been used to change the signs in the numerator.
- There is no need to multiply out the denominator – also note that if the numerator had factorised to $3(x^2 - 1)$ then the factor could have cancelled with an $(x^2 - 1)$ in the denominator. This is one of the reasons to factorise expressions in algebraic fractions.

Now let's get to grips with part (d). The function $g(x)$ is the same as $f'(x)$ which has already been given to us in part (c). The question tells us that the area under the curve from $x = 0$ to $x = a$ is to be called A, and that A = 2. We have to find the value of a. Look at the bottom of page 35 – the question there is exactly the same, but with a simpler function. So we need to integrate $g(x)$, but it's much to complicated for us. But wait a minute: in part (c) we differentiated $f(x)$ to get $g(x)$, so the integral of $g(x)$ must be $f(x)$; we haven't got to do anything clever at all. This underlines how important it is to see how the parts of a question might be related to each other.

(d)   Let $g(x) = f'(x)$. Let A be the area of the region enclosed by the graph of g and the x-axis, between $x = 0$ and $x = a$, where $a > 0$. Given that $A = 2$, find the value of A.

We do not need to include the 2 from $f(x)$ since it will cancel out when we do the subtraction. But if you do include it, the answer will still be the same.

$$A = \int_0^a g(x)dx = \left[\frac{3x}{x^2-1}\right]_0^a = 2$$

$$\frac{3a}{a^2-1} = 2$$

$$3a = 2a^2 - 2$$

$$2a^2 + 3a - 2 = 0$$

$$(2a-1)(a+2) = 0 \Rightarrow a = 0.5 \text{ (since } a > 0)$$

Question 20

The diagram shows the graph of the function f given by

$$f(x) = A\sin\left(\frac{\pi}{2}x\right) + B \text{ for } 0 \le x \le 5, \text{ where } A \text{ and } B \text{ are}$$

constants and x is measured in radians.

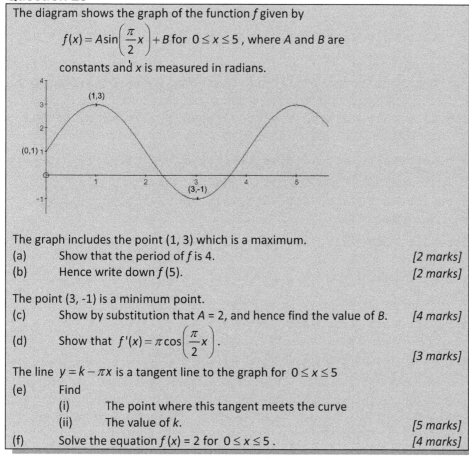

The graph includes the point (1, 3) which is a maximum.

(a)   Show that the period of f is 4.   [2 marks]
(b)   Hence write down $f(5)$.   [2 marks]

The point (3, -1) is a minimum point.

(c)   Show by substitution that $A = 2$, and hence find the value of B.   [4 marks]

(d)   Show that $f'(x) = \pi \cos\left(\frac{\pi}{2}x\right)$.

                                                                                                            [3 marks]

The line $y = k - \pi x$ is a tangent line to the graph for $0 \le x \le 5$

(e)   Find
        (i)   The point where this tangent meets the curve
        (ii)   The value of k.   [5 marks]
(f)   Solve the equation $f(x) = 2$ for $0 \le x \le 5$.   [4 marks]

Analysis: There's a lot in this question. Looking through it we can see that every part refers to $f(x)$, its graph and its derivative. The syllabus sections are under Circular Functions, and particularly sections 3.4 and 3.5 – we need to understand how to deal with this function and, particularly, how the various constants in the function relate to features of the graph. Parts (a) to (d) look fairly straightforward, but that tangent equation in part (e) looks as if it might give us some trouble. In part (d) we will be differentiating, so it's possible that part (e) follows on from that – after all, the gradient of a tangent can be found using the derived function. This, by the way, is a non-calculator question.

> For the function:
> $f(x) = a\sin(bx) + c$
>
> a is the *amplitude* of the wave, that is the vertical distance from maximum to minimum divided by 2
>
> The *period* (the horizontal distance between two equivalent points) is $2\pi / b$
>
> $y = c$ is the line about which the wave oscillates

If you look back over past paper questions you will find quite a few of this type, and they are often linked to a physical situation, such as tidal height or the length of the day.

Answer: In part (a) we need to use the formula for the period shown in the tips box on the right. Why is part (b) a "hence"? Because if we know that the period is 4 then the second maximum will have an x-coordinate of 5, so its y coordinate will also be 3.

The diagram shows the graph of the function f given by

$$f(x) = A\sin\left(\frac{\pi}{2}x\right) + B$$

for $0 \le x \le 5$, where A and B are constants and x is measured in radians. The graph includes the point (1, 3) which is a maximum

(a)   Show that the period of f is 4

$$\text{The period} = \frac{2\pi}{\left(\frac{\pi}{2}\right)} = 2\pi \times \frac{2}{\pi} = \mathbf{4}$$

> (b)　　　Hence write down $f(5)$.
>
> $$f(5) = \mathbf{3}$$

Part (c) ask us to substitute. Substitute what? Well, we have just been told the coordinates of a point, so presumably we need to substitute the point into the equation. However, there are *two* unknowns (A and B). We've been here before: we need to make *two* substitutions, so let's try substituting (1, 3) as well as (3, -1).

> The point (3, -1) is a minimum point.
> (c)　　　Show by substitution that $A = 2$, and hence find the value of B.
>
> $$\text{Substituting (3, -1):}\quad -1 = A\sin\frac{3\pi}{2} + B$$
>
> $$-1 = -A + B \quad (1)$$
>
> $$\text{Substituting (1, 3):}\quad 3 = A\sin\frac{\pi}{2} + B$$
>
> $$3 = A + B \quad (2)$$
>
> $$(2) - (1) \text{ gives } 4 = 2A \text{ so } \mathbf{A = 2}$$
>
> $$\text{Substituting into (2) gives } 3 = 2 + B \text{ so } \mathbf{B = 1}$$

To do this part I needed to be able to convert from radians to degrees and I needed to know sin90° and sin270°. Also note how I labelled the equations (1) and (2) to make it easier to refer to them.

(d):　　　We substitute the values of A and B into the function and then differentiate using the chain rule. Because it's a *show* question, the working must be full and clearly laid out.

(e):　　　The equation of the line, $y = k - \pi x$, looks complicated, but let's take it to bits. In general, the line $y = mx + c$ has gradient m and y-intercept c. In this case, then, the gradient is $-\pi$ and the y-intercept is k. Don't forget that π is a number, so we must be looking for a line which is a tangent to the graph with a specific (negative) gradient. Looking at the graph we see that only the points between (1, 3) and (3, -1) have negative gradients, although in most cases there will be two points with the same gradient. As for (e)(ii), it's not obvious at this stage how we're going to calculate k, so I think all of part (e) is very much a case of "see what happens": the starting point must be to find a point on the graph with gradient $-\pi$.

> (d)　　　Show that $f'(x) = \pi \cos\left(\frac{\pi}{2}x\right)$.
>
> $$f(x) = 2\sin\left(\frac{\pi}{2}x\right) + 1$$
>
> $$f'(x) = 2 \times \frac{\pi}{2}\cos\left(\frac{\pi}{2}x\right)$$
>
> $$= \pi\cos\left(\frac{\pi}{2}x\right)$$

The line $y = k - \pi x$ is a tangent line to the graph for $0 \le x \le 5$

(e)   Find

    (i)   The point where this tangent meets the curve

Tangent meets curve where gradient $= -\pi$

So, $\pi\cos\left(\dfrac{\pi}{2}x\right) = -\pi$

$$\cos\left(\dfrac{\pi}{2}x\right) = -1$$

$$\dfrac{\pi}{2}x = \pi$$

$$x = 2$$

So the tangent meets the curve at **(2, 1)**

    (ii)   The value of k.

Since (2, 1) lies on the line $y = k - \pi x$,

$$1 = k - 2\pi$$

So $k = 2\pi + 1$

So we see that in (e)(ii) it's our old friend substitution again. If an unknown (ie a letter) appears as part of the equation of a line, we have seen that we usually have to substitute a known point into the equation to find the value of the unknown. It's a good idea, once again, to apply the "reasonableness" test to the answer. We think $k = 2\pi + 1$, which is just over 7. Does the intercept of the tangent at (2, 1) look as if it could be about 7? I would say yes to that.

(f): We shall be required to solve a trigonometric equation for this part. Once you get sight of the equation, it's just a matter of tackling it logically using the various techniques available to you. In this case, we just have to simplify the left hand side until we are left with the sin function on its own.

(f)   Solve the equation $f(x) = 2$ for $0 \le x \le 5$.

$$2\sin\left(\dfrac{\pi}{2}x\right) + 1 = 2$$

$$2\sin\left(\dfrac{\pi}{2}x\right) = 1$$

$$\sin\left(\dfrac{\pi}{2}x\right) = \dfrac{1}{2}$$

$$\dfrac{\pi}{2}x = \dfrac{\pi}{6}$$

$$x = \dfrac{1}{3}$$

You will find questions involving trigonometric functions easier if you familiarise yourself with the radian equivalents of 30°, 45°, 60°, 90°, 180° (in particular), and also the exact values of the sin, cos and tan of 0°, 30°, 45°, 60°, 90°.

Now once again, over the page, you'll find some harder algebra questions for you to try yourself.

Question 21

(a)   Let $f(x) = \sin^3 x$

    (i)   Find $f'(x)$, giving your answer in the form

    $a\sin^p x\cos^q x$ where $a, p, q \in \mathbb{Z}$

    (ii)   Let $g(x) = \sqrt{3}\sin x(\cos x)^{\frac{1}{2}}$ for $0 \le x \le \dfrac{\pi}{2}$. Find the

    volume generated when the curve of g is revolved through
2π about the x-axis.   **[8 marks]**

(b)   Let $h(x) = f(x) + \cos^3 x \tan x$, $\dfrac{\pi}{2} < x < \pi$

    (i)   Show that $h(x) = \sin x$

    (ii)   Let $\sin x = \dfrac{2}{3}$. Show that $h(2x) = -\dfrac{4\sqrt{5}}{9}$ **[7 marks]**

Hints: This is a non-calculator question which is why there are so many marks for part (a). Now, each part of this question looks pretty fearsome, whereas much of the question is in fact relatively easy. Partly it's the *look* of the algebra, partly it's the *way* that the questions have been phrased. These hints should help you cut the undergrowth back a bit.

(a)(i)   Don't forget that $\sin^3 x$ is mathematical shorthand for $(\sin x)^3$, and then you can use the chain rule to differentiate. The result should come out in the form that the question requires.

(a)(ii)   This should have something to do with part (i), but what is it? You need to work your way through the method for calculating the volume of revolution: this will require you to square the function g. Just square each part of the function (remembering that $(\cos x)^{\frac{1}{2}}$ is the same as $\sqrt{\cos x}$). You should then see that the function you have to integrate is the same as $f'(x)$ in part (i).

(b)(i)   Write out $h(x)$ in full. We have to simplify this function. One tactic which usually works is to replace $\tan x$ with $\dfrac{\sin x}{\cos x}$. Then simplify the second term, then factorise the expression.

(b)(ii)   What does $h(2x)$ mean? Well , if $h(x) = \sin x$, then $h(2x) = \sin 2x$. So you could rephrase the question as:

$$\text{If } \sin x = \frac{2}{3}, \text{ show that } \sin(2x) = -\frac{4\sqrt{5}}{9}$$

For this, you will need to use two of the trigonometric formulae. The minus sign in the answer is related to the domain of $h(x)$. The roots in the answer arise because you need to work out $\cos x$ from the identity $\sin^2 x + \cos^2 x = 1$.

Answers:

(a)   (i) $f'(x) = 3\sin^2 x \cos x$

    (ii) $V = \pi\displaystyle\int_0^{\frac{\pi}{2}} (\sqrt{3}\sin x\sqrt{\cos x})^2 \, dx$

           $= \pi\displaystyle\int_0^{\frac{\pi}{2}} 3\sin^2 x \cos x \, dx$

           $= \pi\left[\sin^3 x\right]_0^{\frac{\pi}{2}} = \pi$

(b)   (i) $h(x) = \sin^3 x + \cos^3 x \tan x$

$$= \sin^3 x + \cos^3 x \times \frac{\sin x}{\cos x}$$

$$= \sin^3 x + \cos^2 x \sin x$$

$$= \sin x(\sin^2 x + \cos^2 x)$$

$$= \sin x$$

> Whenever you are required to simplify an expression with two terms, always look to see it can be factorised by taking out a common term. In this case we get a very satisfying simplification by doing so.

(b)   (ii) $\sin(2x) = 2\sin x \cos x$

Now, $\cos x = \sqrt{1 - \sin^2 x}$

$$= \sqrt{1 - \left(\frac{2}{3}\right)^2}$$

$$= -\sqrt{\frac{5}{9}} \text{ (since } \frac{\pi}{2} < x < \pi)$$

$$= -\frac{\sqrt{5}}{3}$$

So $\sin(2x) = 2 \times \frac{2}{3} \times \left(-\frac{\sqrt{5}}{3}\right)$

$$= -\frac{4\sqrt{5}}{9}$$

> The cosine of an angle between 90° and 180° is always negative; but the sine of all angles between 0° and 180° is positive. So, although $\sin x = \frac{2}{3}$, we take the negative square root for $\cos x$.

Although this book is all about the long answer questions, I thought at this stage it would be useful for you to try some short answer questions all of which will help you practice algebra.

Given that $\sin x = \frac{1}{3}$, where x is an acute angle, find the **exact** value of:

(a) $\cos x$
(b) $\cos 2x$

Hint: Look up the relevant trigonometric identities. *Exact* means, in this case, using surd notation.

Answers:

(a) $\sqrt{\frac{8}{9}}$ or $\frac{\sqrt{8}}{3}$,   (b) $\frac{7}{9}$

Consider the functions $f : x \to 4(x - 1)$ and $g : x \to \frac{6 - x}{2}$

(a)   Find g^{-1}
(b)   Find $(f \circ g^{-1})$ and simplify your answer

Hint: For part (a) look up the method for working out an inverse function. For part (b) replace the x in function f with function g^{-1}.

Answers:

(a) $g^{-1} : x \to 6 - 2x$,   (b) $(f \circ g^{-1}) : x \to 20 - 8x$

The equation $x^2 - 2kx + 1 = 0$ has two distinct real roots. Find the set of all possible values of k.

Hint: Find the discriminant. This must be greater than 0 for two real roots; solve the resulting inequality. Make sure you know how to solve quadratic inequalities: a very different procedure from solving linear inequalities.

Answer: $k > 1$ or $k < -1$

Solve the equation $\log_3 x - \log_3(x - 5) = 1$

You should also be able to input logarithms to any base using your GDC.

Hint: First, look at the left hand side. It's crying out to be simplified as a single log (using $\log a - \log b = \log\dfrac{a}{b}$). Then use the fact that, in general, if $\log_b x = y$ then $x = b^y$.

Answer: $x = 7.5$

Consider the function $f(x) = \dfrac{x^2 - 3}{e^x}$

(a)   Find $f'(x)$ and simplify your answer as much as possible
(b)   Hence find the x-coordinates of any stationary points.

Hint: Part (a) will be a quotient rule. The simplification is important, and will involve factorising the top line, then simplifying the resulting fraction. In part (b) you must set $f'(x)$ to zero: since it is a fraction, you will only need to set the numerator to zero.

Answer: (a) $\dfrac{2x - x^2 + 3}{e^x}$ (b) $x = 3$ or -1

A group of ten leopards is introduced into a game park. After t years the number of leopards N is modelled by $N = 10e^{0.4t}$
(a)   How many leopards are there after 2 years?
(b)   How long will it take for the number of leopards to reach 100?
Give your answers to an appropriate degree of accuracy.

Hint: For part (a) substitute $t = 2$. For part (b) substitute $N = 100$ and solve for t. In (a) you will not get a whole number result for N so consider what your answer should be, practically. In (b) you could either give an answer to 1DP, or convert that to the whole number of years required.

Answer: (a)   22 leopards,   (b)   5.8 years, so after 6 years.

Given that the function $f(x) = x^2 - 3bx + (c + 2)$, determine the values of b and c such that $f(1) = 0$ and $f'(3) = 0$.

Hint: You will require simultaneous equations to find the values of the two unknowns. The first equation is formed by substituting $f(x) = 0$ when $x = 1$ – it helps to then simplify the equation. Then differentiate (remember to treat b and c as numbers), and substitute $f'(x) = 0$ when $x = 3$.

Answer: $b = 2$, $c = 3$

Question 22

(a)   (i)   Factorise $2\sin^2 x + \sin x - 1$

       (ii)   Hence solve the equation:

$$2\sin^2 x + \sin x - 1 = 0, \ 0 \le x \le 2\pi$$

giving your answers in an **exact** form   *[6 marks]*

Let $f(x) = \frac{1}{2}\sin 2x + \cos x$ for $0 \le x \le 2\pi$. The graph of f is shown below:

There is a maximum point at A and a minimum point at B.

(b)   (i)   Find $f'(x)$ and show that it can be written as

$$1 - \sin x - 2\sin^2 x$$

       (ii)   Write down the values of a and b.   *[5 marks]*

The graph of f first intersects the x-axis at the point with x-coordinate p.

(c)   Show that p lies midway between a and b.   *[2 marks]*

(d)   (i)   Write down an expression involving an integral for the total area enclosed between the curve, the x-axis and the lines $x = a$ and $x = b$.

       (ii)   Calculate this area.   *[4 marks]*

Hints:

(a)   (i)   If you find it hard to factorise a quadratic with trigonometric functions in, try rewriting it with a single letter replacing the function. In this case, $2y^2 + y - 1$. Once factorised, resubstitute $\sin x$ for y.

       (ii)   Note the domain of the function. You should find there are 3 solutions in this domain. You'll see in a moment how you could work this out for yourself.

(b)   (i) $f'(x)$ contains $\cos 2x$. There are three ways of rewriting this function – choose the most appropriate for the question.

       (ii)   A *write down* question, so the answer should be fairly obvious from what we have already done. And we can see that $f'(x)$ is the same as the function in part (a), but with a sign change. And the turning points on the curve will be where $f'(x) = 0$: the equation we solved in (a)(ii). There were 3 solutions there – reference to the diagram shows us which two are a and b, because one of the solutions will refer to the third stationary point – the point of inflexion to the right of B.

(c)   Since we know the values of a and b we can easily calculate the value midway between them. When this is substituted into $f(x)$ we should get zero.

(d)   (i)   Integrating from a to b results in 0. This indicates that the areas above and below the curve are the same. So, to calculate the area, simply find the area from a to p and double it.

       (ii)   This is probably a bit too hard for the non-calculator paper. However, it would be good practice for you to try and work out the integral without a calculator. You will need to know the sine and cosine of several different angles.

Answers:

(a)   (i) $(2\sin x - 1)(x + 1)$,   (ii) $x = \dfrac{\pi}{6}, \dfrac{5\pi}{6}, \dfrac{3\pi}{2}$

(b)   (i) $\cos 2x - \sin x$,   (ii) $a = \dfrac{\pi}{6}, b = \dfrac{5\pi}{6}$

(c)   The mean of $\dfrac{\pi}{6}$ and $\dfrac{5\pi}{6}$ is $\dfrac{3\pi}{6} = \dfrac{\pi}{2}$

    Substituting into $f(x)$: $f\left(\dfrac{\pi}{2}\right) = \dfrac{1}{2}\sin \pi + \cos \dfrac{\pi}{2} = 0$

    Thus p lies midway between a and b

(d)   (i)   Area $= 2 \times \displaystyle\int_{\frac{\pi}{6}}^{\frac{\pi}{2}} \tfrac{1}{2}\sin 2x + \cos x \, dx$, (ii) 1.75

The next question reminds us that a relatively straightforward bookwork question can still give us some complicated algebra.

Question 23

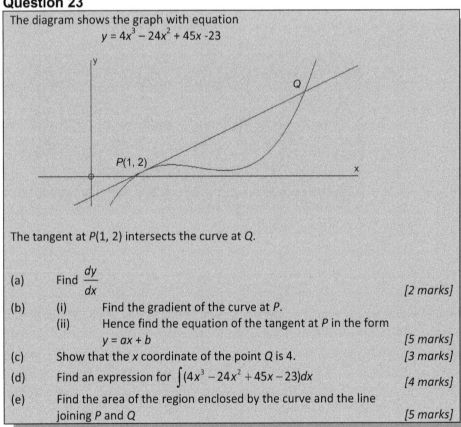

The diagram shows the graph with equation
$$y = 4x^3 - 24x^2 + 45x - 23$$

The tangent at $P(1, 2)$ intersects the curve at Q.

(a)   Find $\dfrac{dy}{dx}$
    [2 marks]

(b)   (i)   Find the gradient of the curve at P.
    (ii)   Hence find the equation of the tangent at P in the form
        $y = ax + b$
    [5 marks]

(c)   Show that the x coordinate of the point Q is 4.
    [3 marks]

(d)   Find an expression for $\displaystyle\int (4x^3 - 24x^2 + 45x - 23)dx$
    [4 marks]

(e)   Find the area of the region enclosed by the curve and the line
    joining P and Q
    [5 marks]

Hints: Parts (a) and (b) should pose no problems for you at all. In part (c), the intersection of two curves can be found by putting their equations equal to each other. In this case the result is a cubic equation, the solution of which is beyond the syllabus. But we can show that $x = 4$ *is* the solution by substituting it into the equation. Part (e) involves the area between two curves. I think the easiest way in this case is to find the area under the straight line by using the formula for the area of a trapezium. Then subtract the area under the curve which can be found by integration.

Answers:

(a) $12x^2 - 48x + 45$

(b)   (i)   9,   (ii) $y = 9x - 7$

(c) $4x^3 - 24x^2 + 45x - 23 = 9x - 7$

     $x = 4$: LHS = 256 – 384 + 180 – 23 = 29; RHS = 36 – 7 = 29

(d) $x^4 - 8x^3 + \dfrac{45}{2}x^2 - 23x + c$

(e)   Area under line = 46.5; area under curve = 19.5. Area between curves = 27

I've included the next question because it's looks so daunting. In fact, you only need to know: Pythagoras' theorem; the cosine rule; the use of the scalar product to find the angle between two lines. And a bit of algebra!

Question 24

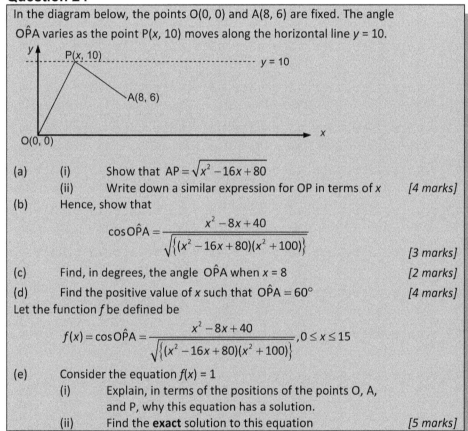

In the diagram below, the points O(0, 0) and A(8, 6) are fixed. The angle OP̂A varies as the point P(x, 10) moves along the horizontal line $y = 10$.

(a)   (i)   Show that $AP = \sqrt{x^2 - 16x + 80}$

     (ii)   Write down a similar expression for OP in terms of x *[4 marks]*

(b)   Hence, show that

$$\cos O\hat{P}A = \frac{x^2 - 8x + 40}{\sqrt{\{(x^2 - 16x + 80)(x^2 + 100)\}}}$$

     [3 marks]

(c)   Find, in degrees, the angle OP̂A when $x = 8$ *[2 marks]*

(d)   Find the positive value of x such that $O\hat{P}A = 60°$ *[4 marks]*

Let the function f be defined be

$$f(x) = \cos O\hat{P}A = \frac{x^2 - 8x + 40}{\sqrt{\{(x^2 - 16x + 80)(x^2 + 100)\}}}, 0 \le x \le 15$$

(e)   Consider the equation $f(x) = 1$

     (i)   Explain, in terms of the positions of the points O, A, and P, why this equation has a solution.

     (ii)   Find the **exact** solution to this equation   *[5 marks]*

> Curly brackets (also called "braces") look like this: { } and are used to enclose expressions which already use ordinary brackets.

Hints: That algebraic fraction in part (b) is enough to put you off immediately and head for the next question. But look, there are only 3 marks for the question, so it can't be too difficult; and we've come across at least part of the expression in part (a) – so we can deduce that the results in part (a) will be used in part (b).

First of all, make sure you understand the situation in the diagram: P moves along the line, O and A are fixed. Angle OP̂A (which appears in every part of the question except (a) and (e)) changes size as P moves.

(a)   How do we calculate the length of a line? By using Pythagoras' Theorem, or by remembering the formula for the distance between two points. For AP, the x distance is $(x - 8)$, the y distance is $(10 - 6)$: pop those into Pythagoras and out pops the required answer. Now do the same for OP (much easier since O is the origin).

(b)   Triangle OPA is not right-angled, so there are two possible ways of calculating $\cos O\hat{P}A$: either using the cosine rule in triangle OAP, or by using the scalar product. I suspect the latter because the triangle hasn't been drawn for us, and part (a) asked us to calculate the lengths of OP and AP. So I suggest you write down the vectors $\overrightarrow{OP}$ and $\overrightarrow{AP}$ and then work from there. Even if you do get stuck, you can still carry on with the rest of the question.

(c)   Substitute $x = 8$. Or, look at the diagram and see where P would be. There's a simple right-angled triangle there which you could use.

(d)   Substituting for $\cos 60°$ will give you a pretty horrific equation to solve – fortunately this is a calculator question.

(e)   (i)   If $f(x) = 1$, what does this mean about angle $O\hat{P}A$? And deduce from that the configuration of the points O, P, and A.
        (ii)   Your calculator will not give you an exact solution, but from the configuration of the points you should be able to work out the value of x using simple ratios. Have a guess first where you think P will be; is your answer a reasonable one?

Answers:

(a)   (i) $AP^2 = (x-8)^2 + 4^2$

$$= x^2 - 16x + 64 + 16$$

$$= x^2 - 16x + 80$$

$$AP = \sqrt{x^2 - 16x + 80}$$

        (ii) $OP^2 = x^2 + 100$

$$OP = \sqrt{x^2 + 100}$$

(b) $\overrightarrow{OP}.\overrightarrow{AP} = \begin{pmatrix} x \\ 10 \end{pmatrix}.\begin{pmatrix} x-8 \\ 4 \end{pmatrix} = \sqrt{x^2 - 16x + 80} \times \sqrt{x^2 + 100} \times \cos O\hat{P}A$

$$x^2 - 8x + 40 = \sqrt{x^2 - 16x + 80} \times \sqrt{x^2 + 100} \times \cos O\hat{P}A$$

$$\cos O\hat{P}A = \frac{x^2 - 8x + 40}{\sqrt{x^2 - 16x + 80}\sqrt{x^2 + 100}}$$

$$\cos O\hat{P}A = \frac{x^2 - 8x + 40}{\sqrt{\{(x^2 - 16x + 80)(x^2 + 100)\}}}$$

(c) $38.7°$

(d) $x = 5.63$

(e)   (i)   O, A and P are in a straight line
        (ii) $x = \dfrac{40}{3}$

If you found it difficult using your calculator to solve the equation – don't worry, help is at hand. In the next chapter.

CALCULATORS AND OTHER ODDITIES

In this chapter we're going to look at those questions which not only require a calculator, but are built around your use of calculator functionality. For example, you may have to sketch the graph of a function after drawing it on your calculator (which will probably involve setting suitable scales); find the zeroes of the function; find turning points; find the equation of a tangent at a point, and where this tangent intersects the graph again; and find the area under a section of the graph. Or you may have to use statistical and probability functions; or manipulate matrices.

And then later on in the chapter I want to take you to the wonderful world of the "one-off" question: where at first glance you think "I don't think I've ever done anything like this before!" How *do* you tackle questions which appear to have left the main road of the syllabus and taken a wrong turning down a little used side road?

First, though, let's look at the following question:

Question 25

The diagram below shows the graph of the function $y = \sin(e^x)$ where $-1 \leq x \leq 2$, and x is in radians. The graph cuts the y-axis at A, and the x-axis at C and D. It has a maximum point at B.

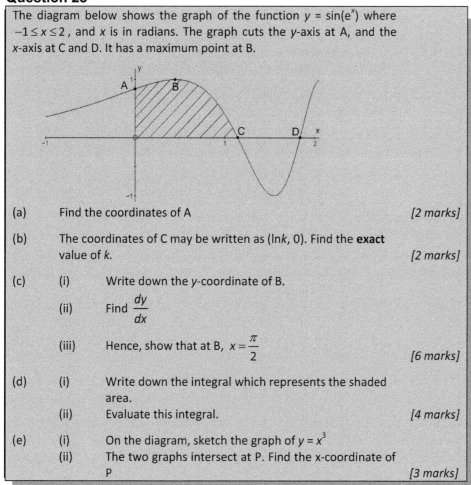

(a)   Find the coordinates of A   *[2 marks]*

(b)   The coordinates of C may be written as $(\ln k, 0)$. Find the **exact** value of k.   *[2 marks]*

(c)   (i)   Write down the y-coordinate of B.

        (ii)   Find $\dfrac{dy}{dx}$

        (iii)   Hence, show that at B, $x = \dfrac{\pi}{2}$ *[6 marks]*

(d)   (i)   Write down the integral which represents the shaded area.

        (ii)   Evaluate this integral.   *[4 marks]*

(e)   (i)   On the diagram, sketch the graph of $y = x^3$

        (ii)   The two graphs intersect at P. Find the x-coordinate of P   *[3 marks]*

Analysis: The clue that this is likely to require calculator skills is in the first line: the function certainly isn't in our standard repertoire. And in (c)(i) we are asked to "write down" the y-coordinate of the maximum without any differentiation. However, and typically in these calculator questions, you won't be doing the *whole* question on the calculator – note the use of the word "exact" in part (b). But you should certainly use your calculator to check such answers. In part (e) we have to sketch a second graph and find the point of intersection of the two graphs – even

I would find solving sin(e^x) = x^3 hard without a calculator: no, not just hard: impossible!

Answer: I suggest that you start the question by drawing the graph of the function on your GDC, using the Window settings to roughly match the axes as shown in the question.

(a)   A is the point where the graph intersects the *y*-axis, so clearly the *x*-coordinate is 0. If we substitute $x = 0$ into the function we find that the *y*-coordinate is sin(e^0) = sin(1). The question tells us that *x* is in radians so we need to find the sine of 1 radian. Clearly a job for the GDC.

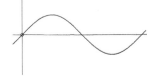

(b)   We need to think through this part logically, and without the GDC since we are asked for an exact value. C is the first point where the graph intersects the *x*-axis, so *y* = 0; that is, we must solve sin(e^x) = 0. Think of the sin graph (see left): the first time $\sin\theta = 0$ is when $\theta = 0$, so $e^x = 0$. But this isn't possible because exponential functions never equal zero. The next time $\sin\theta = 0$ is when $\theta = \pi$, in which case $e^x = \pi$. We need to solve that little equation, and then check that the answer is reasonable.

The diagram below shows the graph of the function $y = \sin(e^x)$ where $-1 \le x \le 2$, and *x* is in radians. The graph cuts the *y*-axis at A, and the *x*-axis at C and D. It has a maximum point at B.

(a)   Find the coordinates of A

> When $x = 0$, $y = \sin(e^0) = \sin 1 = 0.841$
> ∴ **A = (0, 0.841)**

(b)   The coordinates of C may be written as (ln$k$, 0). Find the **exact** value of *k*.

> $y = 0$ so $\sin(e^x) = 0$
> e^x cannot be 0, so $e^x = \pi \Rightarrow x = \ln\pi$
> So, **$k = \pi$**

The *y*-coordinate of A gives us a feeling for the scale on the *y*-axis – this will help us to check later answers are reasonable. Whenever a question involves a graph, or a diagram, it's a good idea to refer your answers back – fill them in on the graph perhaps – so that as you progress through the question your understanding of the situation increases.

If we are right in part (b) then we would expect $\ln\pi$ to be just over 1; in fact the GDC gives it as 1.14. Comforting!

(c)(i)   Use the maximum function on your calculator to find the coordinates of B. Check that both coordinates fit with the information you already have.

(c)(ii)   Use the chain rule since you have a function of a function. If you find this hard then clearly it is an area where more revision is required.

(c)(iii)   Don't forget that for a turning point $\dfrac{dy}{dx} = 0$. But this is a *show that* question: solving an equation on a GDC won't do because we can't show working. Instead we could substitute $x = \ln\dfrac{\pi}{2}$ into the expression for $\dfrac{dy}{dx}$ and show that the result is 0.

(c)   (i)   Write down the y-coordinate of B.

$y = 1$ (GDC)

(ii)   Find $\dfrac{dy}{dx}$

$y = \sin(e^x)$

$u = e^x, \ y = \sin u$

$\dfrac{du}{dx} = e^x, \ \dfrac{dy}{du} = \cos u$

$\dfrac{dy}{dx} = \dfrac{dy}{du} \times \dfrac{du}{dx} = \cos u \times e^x = \cos(e^x) \times e^x$

So $\dfrac{dy}{dx} = e^x \cos(e^x)$

(iii)   Hence, show that at B, $x = \ln\dfrac{\pi}{2}$

If $x = \ln\dfrac{\pi}{2}$ then

$\dfrac{dy}{dx} = e^{\ln\frac{\pi}{2}} \cos e^{\ln\frac{\pi}{2}}$

$= \dfrac{\pi}{2}\cos\dfrac{\pi}{2} = 0$

(d)   Now that we have found the coordinates of C we can write down the required integral. The integration of the function is beyond the scope of this course so must be performed using the GDC

(d)   (i)   Write down the integral which represents the shaded area.

$$\int_0^{\ln\pi} \sin(e^x)\,dx$$

Make sure your calculator is set to radians. *Always* check the mode whenever you are answering a question which involves trigonometric functions.

(ii)   Evaluate this integral.

$$\int_0^{\ln\pi} \sin(e^x)\,dx = 0.906 \ \text{(GDC)}$$

If it's possible to check an area for "reasonableness" then I would encourage you to do so. I normally do this by trying to fit a rectangle around the area. In this case, imagine a rectangle drawn from (0, 0) along to C and up to B. Its height would be 1, its length just over 1. Therefore its area is just over 1, and since the shaded area is just less than the rectangle our answer seems to be just about right.

(e)(i)   You should know the shape of $y = x^3$. Here we must ensure that the graph fits the scales already drawn. $y = x^3$ goes through the points (-1, -1) and (1, 1), and that is enough to enable the sketch to be added.

(e)(ii) This is testing your ability to find the intersection of two graphs on your GDC. The point of intersection will be where $\sin(e^x) = x^3$. The x coordinate will be the solution to the equation; the y-coordinate is irrelevant (in this case).

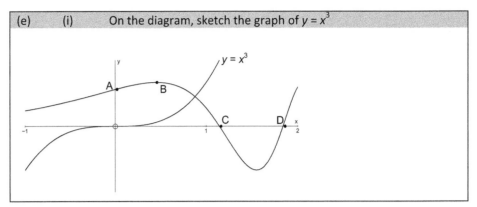

(e) (i) On the diagram, sketch the graph of $y = x^3$

(ii) The two graphs intersect at P. Find the x-coordinate of P

Graphs intersect where $\sin(e^x) = x^3$
Point of intersection is at (0.877, 0.674) (GDC)
So the x co-ordinate of P is **0.877**

If two graphs intersect more than once, you may be asked for a specific point of intersection. Make sure you know how to do this on your GDC.

In question 6 we saw that Normal probability problems are always answered using your GDC. This one is rather more complicated, so we're going to have to work out just what calculations to do.

Question 26

This question concerns the heights of all 14 year old students in a large school. The girls' heights are normally distributed with mean 155cm and standard deviation 10cm. The boys' heights are normally distributed with mean 160cm and standard deviation 12cm.

(a) Find the probability that a girl is taller than 170cm. *[2 marks]*

(b) A girl is chosen at random. Given that she is taller than 170cm, what is the probability that she is taller than 175cm. *[3 marks]*

(c) Given that 10% of girls are shorter than x cm, find x to the nearest cm. *[3 marks]*

(d) Given that 90% of boys have heights between a and b cm, where a and b are symmetrical about 160cm, and $a < b$, find the values of a and b. *[4 marks]*

(e) In a group of 10 boys, what is the probability that at least 7 are over 165cm *[4 marks]*

Analysis: There are no *show that* keywords in this question, and since we will be doing it all on the calculator that is probably just as well. A curious feature of this question is that the words "given that" appear in parts (b), (c), and (d). In a probability question this almost always means conditional probability. But read through each part: only one of them involves conditional probability – can you see which? Now read part (e) right through – how would you tackle this question? It has all the hallmarks of a binomial probability question – what are those hallmarks? Read on to find out!

Answers: Part (a) is a straightforward Normal probability calculation. You need to enter four parameters into your GDC: the mean, standard deviation, lower bound and upper bound. Make sure you know which order to put them in. The upper bound in this case is infinity, but using a large number such as 1000 (in this case) will work just as well. Try them both on your GDC to check. Note that in my answer I calculate the Z value of 170cm – you should always show *some* working when using your GDC.

This question concerns the heights of all 14 year old students in a large school. The girls' heights are normally distributed with mean 155cm and standard deviation 10cm. The boys' heights are normally distributed with mean 160cm and standard deviation 12cm.

(a)   Find the probability that a girl is taller than 170cm.

> 170cm is 1.5 standard deviations above the mean
> P(girl is taller that 170cm) = 0.0668 (GDC)

It's worth remembering that about 16% of values are above 1 standard deviation over the mean (from which it follows that about one third are *within* 1 standard deviation), and 2% are above 2 standard deviations. In this case we get a probability of about 7%, which fits very well with these values.

Part (b) is the first of the "given that" questions, and is also the conditional probability. You can tell because the form of the question is: "Given that ...... find the probability that ......", whereas parts (c) and (d) don't ask you to calculate probabilities. The conditional probability formula is stated in question 14 – how does it work in this case? We need: $\dfrac{\text{P(she is taller than 175cm AND she is taller than 170cm)}}{\text{P(she is taller than 170cm)}}$

The top line doesn't immediately seem logical, but boils down to the probability that the girl is taller than 175cm. So we must calculate:

$$\frac{\text{P(she is taller than 175cm)}}{\text{P(she is taller than 170cm)}}$$

(b)   A girl is chosen at random. Given that she is taller than 170cm, what is the probability that she is taller than 175cm.

> 175cm is 2 standard deviations above the mean
> P(girl is taller than 175cm) = 0.0228 (GDC)
>
> P(girl is taller than 175cm | she is taller than 170cm) = $\dfrac{.0228}{.0668}$
>
> = **0.341**

Part (c) is very similar to part (c) in question 6. In that question I suggested that a sketch would help you understand the situation better – here's my sketch.

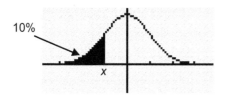

You can get straight to the result but again it would be sensible to show some of the intermediate working, or even the complete calculation - especially when you consider that there are 3 marks. Make sure that if a specific accuracy is requested that you do as asked – if you don't then you deserve the lost mark!

<table>
<tr><td>(c)</td><td>Given that 10% of girls are shorter than x cm, find x to the nearest cm.</td></tr>
</table>

For a lower area of 10%, $Z = -1.282$ (GDC)

$$Z = \frac{x - \mu}{\sigma}$$

$$-1.282 = \frac{x - 155}{10}$$

$$x = 155 - 12.82$$

So $x = 142.18 \approx$ **142cm**

To find the Z value, use an appropriate function on your calculator (such as invNorm on the TI series).

Part (d) looks complicated: let's try to simplify it by taking the question apart. We are looking for two values which are symmetrically placed either side of the mean – well, that's good, because once we've found one of them the other can be written down. Now between these two values we will find 90% of the boys, so that's 45% above the mean and 45% below. So let's take the upper value: 45% above the mean is the same as 95% from the start of the distribution. So the value of b is the height below which there are 95% of boys – and we can see that the question is very similar to part (c). And notice that I have calculation this time – I've already shown that I can do it.

45%   45%

95%

Area=.866386
low=-1.5   Iup=1.5

<table>
<tr><td>(d)</td><td>Given that 90% of boys have heights between a and b cm, where a and b are symmetrical about 160cm, and a < b, find the values of a and b.</td></tr>
</table>

For an area of 95%, $Z = 1.645$ (GDC)
With $\mu = 160$ and $\sigma = 12$, $x = 179$cm (GDC)
So **b = 179** and **a = 141**

Now, what do we have in part (e)? If we want the probability that 7 out of 10 things had a certain property, this would be a binomial probability. So at least 7 out of 10 is a cumulative binomial probability. The GDC calculates cumulatives from 0 upwards, so we need to calculate the probability of up to 6 boys being taller that 165cm and then subtract the answer from 1 (giving us 7 or more). First, then, we must calculate the probability of *one* boy being taller than 165cm – this, of course, is a Normal probability calculation.

The wording is crucial:

P(at least 7) is calculated as:
1 – P(up to 6)

P(more than 7) is calculated as: 1 – P(up to 7)

<table>
<tr><td>(e)</td><td>In a group of 10 boys, what is the probability that at least 7 are over 165cm</td></tr>
</table>

$$Z = \frac{165 - 160}{12} = 0.417$$

$P(x > 165) = 0.338$ (GDC)

P(at least 7 out of 10 > 165cm) = 1 – P(fewer than 7 are > 165cm)

$= 1 - 0.979$

$= $ **0.031**

Now for four more questions which require you to demonstrate your calculator techniques. Some hints for you as usual.

IBDP Mathematics SL: Section B Questions

Question 27

The function f is defined as $f(x) = (2x+1)e^{-x}$, $0 \leq x \leq 3$. The point A(0, 1) lies on the graph of $f(x)$, and there is a maximum point at B.

(a)   Sketch the graph of $y = f(x)$, labelling the points A and B.   *[3 marks]*

(b)   (i)   Show that $f'(x) = (1-2x)e^{-x}$

      (ii)   Find the **exact** coordinates of B.   *[7 marks]*

(c)   The equation $f(x) = k$, where $k \in \mathbb{R}$, has two solutions. Write down the range of values of k.   *[2 marks]*

(d)   Given that $f''(x) = e^{-x}(-3+2x)$, show that the curve of f has only one point of inflexion.   *[2 marks]*

(e)   Let C be the point on the curve of f with x-coordinate 3. Find the area of the curve enclosed by the curve and the line AC.   *[7 marks]*

Hints: The whole question revolves around the function $f(x)$ and its graph, so make sure you start by entering it accurately into your calculator, and drawing it with a sensible range of values for both x and y. Parts (b) and (e) each carry 7 marks – we'll see why in a moment.

(a)   Copy the graph from your calculator. Make sure your sketch is a good size (at least a quarter of a page), and that you clearly mark the key points, including any axis intercepts. Note the domain: your sketch should not go beyond.

In (b) you have to differentiate the function (using the chain rule – be careful with all the minus signs) and then find the coordinates of the maximum; a standard bookwork question, but with quite a difficult function. At least with the calculator to hand you can easily check if our answer is correct.

(c)   If you draw the line $y = k$ on your graph, it will intersect the curve where $f(x) = k$. So you need to examine your graph and imagine a horizontal line moving up and down – between which two values will this line intersect the graph exactly twice.

(d)   Bookwork – how are points of inflexion defined algebraically?

In (e) you have to find the area enclosed between a line and the curve. Look back to question 23 to see how we did it there.

Answers:

(a)

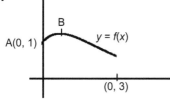

(b)(i) $f'(x) = (2x+1) \times (-e^{-x}) + 2e^{-x} = e^{-x}(-2x-1+2) = (1-2x)e^{-x}$

    (ii)   B = $(0.5, 2e^{-0.5})$

(c) $1 \leq k < 2e^{-0.5}$

> In (c) we cannot include the y-coordinate at B as a possible value of k since the line and the curve only intersect once, not twice.

(d) $e^{-x}(-3 + 2x) = 0$ has only one solution, $x = 1.5$

(e)   Area under curve = $\int_0^3 (2x+1)e^{-x}dx = 2.552$ (GDC)

    C = $(3, 7e^{-3})$, so area under line = $3 \times \frac{1}{2}(1+7e^{-3}) = 2.023$

    So area enclosed by curve and AC = 2.522 – 2.023 = 0.320

> The area under the line can be found using the formula for the area of a trapezium.

Question 28

A manufacturer records the sales, *y* thousands, of 10 different products over 6 months, and the amount, *x*, in hundreds of pounds spent on advertising. The following table shows the results:

x	7.3	39	16.5	16	44	30.5	35.5	26.5	4.5	20
y	15	50	30	21	48.5	45	38	35	13	29.5

(a)   (i)   Draw a scatter diagram to illustrate the data.
       (ii)   What does the diagram suggest about the correlation between *x* and *y*?   *[4 marks]*

(b)   (i)   Calculate the correlation coefficient for the data.
       (ii)   Find the regression line of *y* on *x*, and add to the graph.
       (iii)   Hence estimate the sales which might result from an advertising expenditure of £2400.   *[6 marks]*

(c)   (i)   If the mean values of *x* and *y* are *m* and *n* respectively, show that (*m*, *n*) lies on the regression line.
       (ii)   Give an interpretation of the coefficients in your equation.
                                           [5 marks]

Hints: This is actually a fairly straightforward bookwork question entirely taken from syllabus section 5.4, but I have included it to ensure that you can use your GDC for calculations involving correlation and related matters. Make sure that you enter the data accurately into the lists, and that you know how to access the relevant calculations.

(a)   We have not been asked to draw the line of best fit, just the points. Make sure your axes and scales are clearly labelled. It is unlikely that in a question of this type there will be no correlation: if that were the case, there would be no more which could be asked! The terms describing correlation are *strong*, *moderate*, and *weak*; and correlation is either *positive* or *negative*.

All of part (b) is done on the GDC, and it all depends on you having entered the data correctly. Double check every time.

In (c), a regression line will always go through the point representing the two means. In fact, the equation can be written as $(y - \bar{y}) = m(x - \bar{x})$. You will need to calculate the means by using one-variable statistical calculations on each of the two lists. In the last part, consider what the gradient and *y*-intercept of a straight line usually mean in practical situations.

Answers:

(a)   (i)
       (ii)   Strong positive correlation.

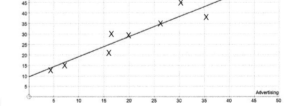

(b)   (i)   0.958
       (ii)   *y* = 0.955*x* + 9.61
       (iii)   *x* = 24, *y* = 32.53. So, sales of about 32500.

(c)   (i)   *m* = 23.98, *n* = 32.5
                0.955 × 23.98 + 9.61 = 32.51, thus (*m*, *n*) lies on the line.
       (ii)   On average, we can expect sales of 9600 in a month without advertising, rising by 9555 for every £100 spent.

Question 29

There were 1100 doctors working in a city on 1 January 1990. After t years the number of doctors, d, working in the city is given by:

$$d = 1100 + 50t + 2t^2$$

(a)   (i)   How many doctors were working in the city at the start of 2000?

         (ii)   In what year were there first more than 1500 doctors working in the city?   *[4 marks]*

At the beginning of 1990 the city had a population of 1.2 million. After t years the population, P, of the city is given by:

$$P = 1\,200\,000(1.02)^t$$

(b)   (i)   Find the population at the beginning of 2000, giving your answer to an appropriate degree of accuracy.

         (ii)   Calculate the percentage growth of the population between the start of 1990 and the start of 2000.

         (iii)   In what year was the population first greater than 1.5 million?   *[7 marks]*

(c)   (i)   What was the mean number of people per doctor at the start of 1990?

         (ii)   At what rate was the mean number of people per doctor falling in 1990?

         (iii)   At what average rate did the mean number of people per doctor decline between 1990 and 2005?   *[7 marks]*

Hints: This question involves making sense of two functions. You will need to find values of the functions, solve equations and find rates of change. When performing several calculations with functions I find it easier to enter them to the GDC and then use the Y variables as "shortcuts". If you're not sure how to do this I do urge you to find out.

(a)   In question 1 I pointed out that in many situations involving functions you are required first to substitute a value for x to calculate the corresponding function value; and then, given a value of the function, work out x by solving an equation. This is exactly what you have to in parts (i) and (ii) here. Just be careful in part (ii): solving the equation $1500 = 1100 + 50t + 2t^2$ gives you a value for t. You must now interpret that to say in which year there were more than 1500 doctors.

If you solve the equation in (a)(ii) using a graph you must ensure that the window includes the solution – you can use a table of values to help you choose a window. Or you can use the calculator's solve function to save having to draw the graph.

Another way to solve this is to create a table of the function. Start the table at $x = 1$, increment in steps of 1, and this is the result (see right).

Thus there were 1472 doctors at the start of 1996 and 1548 at the start of 1997.

X	Y₁	Y₂
1	1152	1.22E6
2	1208	1.25E6
3	1268	1.27E6
4	1332	1.3E6
5	1400	1.32E6
6	1472	1.35E6
7	1548	1.38E6

(b)   Parts (i) and (iii) ask you to do exactly the same as in part (a), except with a different function. In part (i) the "appropriate degree of accuracy" can be gauged by consideration of the initial population figure as quoted in the question. In part (iii) you could either use logs to solve algebraically or solve on the GDC; or, again, use a table.

(c)   Now we have to combine the two functions. I find that the easiest way to work out what to do is to remember that "per" is the same as "divide". So, the number of people per doctor can be found by dividing the number of people by the number of doctors. And since we have to do several calculations, we could again use the Y variables on the GDC. If Y_1 is the number of people, P, and Y_2 is the number of doctors, d, then you could set $Y_3 = Y_2/Y_1$ for the mean number of people per doctor. In part (ii), draw the graph of Y_3 and find $\dfrac{dy}{dx}$ when $t = 0$.

Part (iii) looks complicated because we have the word "average" and the word "mean" in the same sentence. But the "mean number of people per doctor" is the same function we have been dealing with in (c)(i) and (ii): all we have to do is calculate that value in 1990 and 2005, and then divide the difference by 15.

Answers:

(a)	(i)	1800	(ii)	1996		
(b)	(i)	1.46 million	(ii)	21.9%	(iii)	2001
(c)	(i)	1091	(ii)	28	(iii)	25.9

The next three questions are really "one-offs". They don't fall into any category because they are unique. You'll look at them and say: "I've never done one quite like this before." True. And you'll probably never do one quite like it again! But practising these questions is certainly useful.

What can we learn from such questions? First, identify the topic(s) on which the question is based. Second, try and reduce the question to the normal techniques and calculations with which you are familiar. Overall you may need to apply a bit of lateral thinking.

I'm not going to start with analysis and worked examples simply because these *are* one-offs: it's unlikely that any analysis could then be applied to other questions. So let's dive straight into the practice questions – hints and answers as usual.

Question 30

In a simple pattern of dots, each row has one less dot than the row above. For example, a pattern which starts with a row of 4 dots will contain 10 in total.

(a)   Show that a pattern which has 40 dots in the top row contains 820 dots in total.   *[3 marks]*

(b)   Another pattern has 3240 dots in total. How many dots are in the top row?   *[4 marks]*

(c)   (i)   Suppose that in general there are T dots in a similar pattern, with n in the top row.

                Show that $n^2 + n - 2T = 0$.

        (ii)   Hence explain why 3000 dots cannot be organised in such a pattern.   *[6 marks]*

(d)   Calculate how many dots there will be in a pattern which has 400 dots in the top row and 200 in the bottom.   *[3 marks]*

Hints: A look at part (a) soon tells us that this question is about arithmetic series. With 40 dots in the top row, 39 in the next and so on, the total will be 40 + 39 + 38 + ... + 1. Time to brush up your sequences and series formulae which we last met in question 10. And, as I mentioned there, always check carefully: do you need the formula for the nth term, or the formula for the sum to n terms?

(a) You might prefer to think of the series as 1 + 2 + 3 + ... + 40. There are two versions of the formula for the sum of an arithmetic progression – one of them involves the nth term, the other doesn't. Have we got the nth term (ie the last term) of the series? Yes, it's 40 – so use the appropriate formula.

(b) Let's analyse what information we know.

$$S_n = 3240$$
$$u_1 = 1$$
$$d = 1$$

So let's use the formula $S_n = \dfrac{n}{2}(2u_1 + (n - 1)d)$ to find n, and hence the number of dots in the top row.

(c) (i) Try using the same formula and substituting the variables in the question.
(ii) So what happens if $T = 3000$?

(d) A couple of possible approaches here. You could find the sum of the series which starts at 200 and finishes at 400 (be careful when counting the number of terms). Or use the formula in part (c) twice: first with $n = 400$ and then again with $n = 199$, subtracting the results. Think carefully: why not $n = 200$?

Answers:

(a) $S_{40} = \dfrac{40}{2}(2 \times 1 + 39 \times 1) = 820$

(b) $3240 = \dfrac{n}{2}(2 \times 1 + (n - 1) \times 1)$

$6480 = n(n + 1) \Rightarrow n = 80$ (GDC)

(c) (i) $T = \dfrac{n}{2}(2 \times 1 + (n - 1) \times 1)$

$2T = n(1 + n)$

$n^2 + n - 2T = 0$

(ii) $n^2 + n - 4200 = 0$ has positive solution $n = 64.3$, so no integer solution is possible.

(d) 60300

In question 31 we return to kinematics and associated calculus. It's a non-calculator question, so do give some thought as to how you would lay out your answer.

Question 31

The acceleration, a ms^{-2}, of a particle at time t seconds is given by:

$$a = 2t + 2\cos t$$

(a)	Find the acceleration of the particle at $t = 0$.	[2 marks]
(b)	Find the velocity, v, at time t, given that the initial velocity of the particle is 2ms^{-1}.	[4 marks]
(c)	Find $\int_0^3 v\,dt$, giving your answer in the form $p - q\cos3$.	[6 marks]
(d)	What information does the answer to part (c) give about the motion of the particle?	[3 marks]

Hints:

Remember that sin0 = 0 but cos0 = 1.

The only other kinematics questions in this book is number 1, but that was pretty straightforward compared to this one. That question only involved differentiation because we needed to find a function for velocity given a function for distance. In this one we know the acceleration, and wish to find velocity; that must involve integration. The diagram below may be a useful aide-memoire.

————————————— DIFFERENTIATE —————————————▶
Displacement (or height) s ----- Velocity v ----- Acceleration a
◀————————————— INTEGRATE —————————————

So in part (b) we will integrate to find a velocity function, and it seems that in part (c) we will need to integrate this function, presumably giving us a new function defining the particle's displacement from the origin, or its position. But don't expect it to be entirely straightforward – there are 6 marks involved.

(b)   Don't forget that when integrating a function there will be a constant of integration. In applied questions such as these we need to look for the information which will enable us to calculate the constant: in this case, we use the initial velocity – that is, when $t = 0$, $v = 2$.

(c)   Now we have a definite integral so the constant of integration is not necessary. This is a non-calculator paper; even so, if it had appeared in a calculator paper we would still have to do the integration manually so as to arrive at the required form. Note that this involves cos3 rather than cos$k$, say; a little bit of help from the examiner so that we can see we are on the right lines. As ever, be careful with minus signs.

(d)   Be careful with your interpretation. There is a big difference between "displacement", which is change in position from the start of the time period to the end, and "distance travelled". For example, a particle could travel 3m out from the origin and 3m back in 4 seconds. Its displacement would be 0m (with an average velocity of 0ms^{-1}), but distance travelled would be 6m (with average speed 1.5ms^{-1}).

Also note that position of the particle at $t = 0$ is not necessarily the origin. There is not enough information given to know what it is in this question.

Answers:

(a)   1ms^{-2}

(b) $(t^2 + 2\sin t + 2)$ ms^{-1}

(c) $\left[\dfrac{t^3}{3} - 2\cos t + 2t\right]_0^3 = 17 - 2\cos3$

(d)   In the first three seconds, the particle has changed position by $(13 - 2\cos6)$ m.

Question 32

The following diagram shows a semicircle centre O, diameter [QR], with radius 3. Let P be a point on the circumference, with θ in radians.

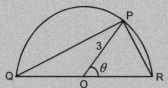

(a)   Find the area of triangle OPR, in terms of θ *[2 marks]*

(b)   Explain why the area of triangle OPQ is the same as the area of triangle OPR.   *[3 marks]*

Let A be the total area of the two segments shaded in the diagram below.

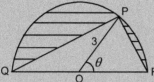

(c)   Show that $A = \dfrac{9}{2}(\pi - 2\sin\theta)$ *[3 marks]*

(d)   (i)   Find the value of θ when A is a local minimum, justifying that it is a minimum.

        (ii)   Find this minimum area, giving your answer in an **exact** form.   *[8 marks]*

Hints: There are many things to remember when dealing with the geometry of a circle. One of the more important is to identify any radii, because they are all the same length; and because of this, you will often find isosceles triangles lurking inside a circle (or a semicircle).

(a)   There are two formulae for the area of a triangle (see right). Which do you think is the more relevant here?

> Area $= \dfrac{1}{2} \times \text{base} \times \text{height}$
>
> Area $= \dfrac{1}{2} ab \sin\theta$

(b)   You could explain this using *either* of the two area formulae.

(c)   In this type of question you are often asked to find the area of an irregular shaded shape. It is almost always the case that you do this by finding the difference of two simpler shapes – in this case, the semicircle and the triangle.

(d)   (i)   What does "minimum" suggest to you. Differentiation, I hope. And find the second derivative to test that you have a minimum, not a maximum

Answers:

(a) $\dfrac{9}{2}\sin\theta$

(b)   The bases of the triangles are equal (OQ = OR) and they have the same height. Thus they have the same area.

         or

    The area of OQR is $\dfrac{9}{2}\sin(180 - \theta)$. Since $\sin(180 - \theta) = \sin\theta$ this is the same as the area of triangle OPR.

(c)   Semicircle – triangle $= \dfrac{9\pi}{2} - 2 \times \dfrac{9}{2}\sin\theta = \dfrac{9}{2}(\pi - 2\sin\theta)$

(d)   (i) $\theta = \dfrac{\pi}{2}, \dfrac{d^2A}{d\theta^2} = 9\sin\theta > 0$ (ii) $\dfrac{9\pi}{2} - 9$

MID IBDP SUMMER PROGRAMMES

OSC

Summary

Who is it for?
For students entering their final year
of the IB Diploma Programme

Locations include:
Harvard and MIT, USA
Cambridge, UK

Duration
Min. 1 week, max. 6 weeks
1 or 2 IB subjects per week

Improve confidence and
grades

Highly-experienced IB
teachers and examiners

Tailored classes to meet
students' needs

Wide range of available
subjects

Safe accommodation and
24-hour pastoral care

Features

- Morning teaching in chosen IB subject
- 2nd IB subject afternoon classes
- IB Skills afternoon classes
- One-to-one Extended Essay Advice, Private Tuition and University Guidance options
- Small classes
- Daily homework
- Unique IB university fair
- Class reports for parents
- Full social programme.

By the end of their first year, students understand the stimulating and challenging nature of the IB Diploma.

They also know that the second year is crucial in securing the required grades to get into their dream college or university.

This course helps students to avoid a 'summer dip' by using their time effectively. With highly-experienced IB teachers, we consolidate a student's year one

learning, close knowledge gaps, and introduce some year two material.

In a relaxed environment, students develop academically through practice revision and review. They are taught new skills, techniques, and perspectives – giving a real boost to their grades. This gives students an enormous amount of confidence and drive for their second year.

"The whole experience was incredible. The university setting was inspiring, the friends I made, and the teaching was first-class. I feel so much more confident in myself and in my subject.

OSC Student

Please note that locations and course features are subject to change - please check our website for up-to-date details.

Find out more: 🏠 osc-ib.com/mid 📱 +44 (0)1865 512802